A Beginner's Guide to Differential Forms

First published 2021

Published by Incomprehensible Books

Peter Collier asserts the moral right to be identified as the author of this work

ISBN 9780957389472

10 9 8 7 6 5 4 3 2

Email: incomprehensiblething@gmail.com

A Beginner's Guide to Differential Forms

Peter Collier

Incomprehensible Books

For Anne

Contents

Preface

There is an intriguing class of mathematical objects, called differential forms, that live on manifolds, eat tangent vectors and spit out numbers, and do this in a way that makes them of great interest to mathematicians and physicists. Arfken et al. [3], authors of *Mathematical Methods for Physicists: A Comprehensive Guide*, comment:

> The calculus of differential forms, of which the leading developer was Elie Cartan, has become recognized as a natural and very powerful tool for the treatment of curved coordinates, both in classical settings and in contemporary studies of curved spacetime. Cartan's calculus leads to a remarkable unification of concepts and theorems of vector analysis that is worth pursuing, with the result that in differential geometry and in theoretical physics the use of differential forms is now widespread.

And this is from *Vector Calculus, Linear Algebra, and Differential Forms: A Unified Approach* by Hubbard and Hubbard [11]:

> Because forms work in any dimension, they are the natural way to approach two towering subjects that are inherently four-dimensional: electromagnetism and the theory of relativity. They also provide a unified treatment of differentiation and of the fundamental theorem of calculus: one operator (the exterior derivative) works in all dimensions, and one short, elegant statement (the generalized Stokes's theorem) generalizes the fundamental theorem of calculus to all dimensions. In contrast, vector calculus requires special formulas, operators, and theorems for each dimension where it works.

I first came across differential forms some years ago when I was taking my first baby steps in studying relativity theory[1]. An infinitesimal displacement in spacetime can be represented either as a tangent vector or a 1-form, dual objects linked by a function called the metric tensor. Not having much in the way of a mathematical imagination, I found there to be a whiff of magic to these mysterious 1-forms that were part of the machinery used to describe the structure of curved spaces. And if 1-forms were perplexing, what on earth was the story behind their weightier relatives – 2-forms, 3-forms, n-forms? Fast forward a few years, and with the differential forms bee still buzzing around in my head, I thought it would be fun to investigate these strange objects further.

I'm not a mathematician, however, and I found much of the mathematical literature to be so overwhelming and abstract as to be useless for the purposes of self-study. The

---

[1]Shameless plug – the result of my labours was a book: *A Most Incomprehensible Thing: Notes Towards a Very Gentle Introduction to the Mathematics of Relativity* (ISBN 9780957389465).

'Intrinsic definition' of differential forms given in the Wikipedia article, for example, includes stuff like $\beta_p \in \bigwedge^k T_p^\star M$ and $\beta_p : \bigoplus_{n=1}^{k} T_p M \to \mathbb{R}$, both of which I'm sure are crystal clear to a mathematics graduate but are way above my head.

So not being a mathematician, I knew I wouldn't be able to master differential forms to an advanced level. For the foreseeable future at least, $\beta_p : \bigoplus_{n=1}^{k} T_p M \to \mathbb{R}$ would remain a mystery to me. However, I'm a firm believer that given sufficient enthusiasm, a little maths education can go a long way. With that optimistic philosophy in mind, my goal was to achieve a basic working understanding of the subject matter – what are differential forms? how are they manipulated? what are they used for? In the hope that others might share my interest, the notes I put together during my studies eventually morphed into this little book, which is aimed at those readers who may not be maths whizzes but who are interested in tackling a relaxed but wide-ranging introduction to differential forms.

The only prerequisite – apart from the aforementioned enthusiasm – is a reasonable foundation in advanced, school-level mathematics. So ideally you should be familiar with basic algebra and sufficient multivariable calculus to be at ease with partial derivatives and double and triple integrals. Some vector analysis would also be useful, as would a little bit of matrix algebra. We make many references to manifolds, but mostly only at the most elementary level as smooth curves, surfaces and higher dimensional spaces embedded in some Euclidean $\mathbb{R}^n$. Because my target audience is only a small maths-step up from the general reader, I've attempted to make verbosity a virtue, giving what I consider to be important derivations in full, even at the risk of stating and restating what is blindingly obvious to the more mathematically astute.

The emphasis for much of this book will be on how differential forms provide an alternative means of understanding three-dimensional vector calculus. For those readers unfamiliar with the basics of vector calculus I summarise the key concepts as we encounter them. Worked examples are a great way of consolidating mathematical understanding, so I've included a number of such problems in the text. Where possible, I've included code that you can copy into the WolframAlpha online calculator [22] to check your answers.

We start with a short review of essential background material and notation. Next we look at differential forms and what we mean when we say they are linear or, more generally, multilinear alternating functions of tangent vectors. We then look at how differential forms correspond with various scalar and vector fields; how to differentiate forms; and how to express in the language of differential forms the three important operators of vector analysis – grad, curl and div. Differential forms are integrated over *oriented* manifolds, so we then briefly discuss the notion of orientation. Differential forms are the answer to the question: what objects do we integrate on manifolds? 1-forms are the natural things to integrate along a curve, 2-forms over a surface, and so on. Therefore, we next move on to integrating differential forms, in the process seeing how forms can be used to easily derive the change of variables formula. We then relate what we have learned to the line, surface and volume integrals of vector calculus.

These integrals are themselves the building blocks of the big four vector calculus theorems: the gradient theorem, Green's theorem, Stokes' theorem and the divergence theorem. In turn, these four theorems are themselves special cases of the generalised Stokes' theorem – what Schulz and Schulz [18] refers to as 'one of the triumphs of elementary mathematics' – that applies to spaces of arbitrary dimension and which we discuss in chapter 9. Next we turn to Maxwell's equations, the foundation of classical electromagnetic theory. We discuss what these equations are, what they mean, and how, using differential forms, they can be pleasingly reduced to just two concise formulations. Finally, we see how the generalised Stokes' theorem can be used to prove three rather neat topological theorems: the drum theorem, the Brouwer fixed-point theorem and the famous hairy ball theorem ('you can't comb a hairy ball smooth').

Acknowledgements

I am greatly indebted to David L. Finn (Associate Professor of Mathematics at Rose-Hulman Institute of Technology), who was kind enough to read through my manuscript and provide invaluable comments and feedback. As ever, of course, any remaining errors are my own.

Also, post-publication, thank you to those readers who were kind enough to tell me about some of those remaining errors.

- Comments and suggestions? Email the author at incomprehensiblething@gmail.com.
- This book was written using LyX, an excellent maths-friendly (and much more) open source document preparation system based on LaTeX.

My apologies if any acknowledgement or bibliographic citation has been inadvertently omitted. Please contact me and I will be pleased to make the necessary arrangements at the earliest opportunity.

1 Preliminaries

Before we can begin our discussion of differential forms, we need to run through some essential background material and notation

1.1 Manifolds

Differential forms live on manifolds. So, what's a manifold?

Answer: as far as we're concerned, they're simply smooth (ie differentiable) spaces that are locally Euclidean. The surface of the Earth, for example, is not Euclidean (for the sake of argument we'll ignore the bumps and dips and assume our planet is perfectly spherical). Lines of longitude that start off parallel meet at the poles; the sum of the interior angle of a triangle need not add up to $180°$; and the Pythagorean theorem does not hold. However, a small enough patch of a sphere's surface is pretty much flat, ie Euclidean. (Mathematicians are able to formalise the notion of 'pretty much flat'.) The sphere is a two-dimensional manifold. Why two-dimensional? Because any point on the surface of a sphere can be described using a minimum of two coordinates – longitude and latitude, for example.

Circles and smooth (non-crossing) curves are examples of one-dimensional manifolds – small enough segments look like straight lines and points on them can be described using a single coordinate.

One of the simplest manifolds is $\mathbb{R}^n$, which denotes n-dimensional Euclidean space. $\mathbb{R}^2$ is two-dimensional, like a flat piece of paper. $\mathbb{R}^3$ is three-dimensional, like the space we live in. Higher dimensional spaces ($n > 3$) are perfectly acceptable though hard for most of us to visualise.

Draw a smooth curve on a flat piece of paper and you have embedded a one-dimensional manifold (the curve) in two-dimensional Euclidean space $\mathbb{R}^2$ (the flat piece of paper). A smoothly curved piece of zero-thickness wire lying on a table represents a one-dimensional manifold (the wire) embedded in our own everyday three-dimensional Euclidean space $\mathbb{R}^3$. A ball sitting next to the wire represents a two-dimensional manifold (the surface of the ball) embedded in $\mathbb{R}^3$. Embedded manifolds such as these are nice and easy to visualise and are the ones we'll mainly be looking at. However, manifolds don't have to be embedded in some higher dimensional space and, though more abstract to describe, are perfectly capable of existing in their own right.

In relativity theory, spacetime is a four-dimensional (non-Euclidean) manifold – three of space, one of time.

We'll only be concerned with orientable manifolds – in chapter 6 we discuss what it means for a manifold to be orientable.

Here are some of the convention's we'll be making use of:

- The letter C denotes a smooth curve, which can exist in any dimension.

- The letter S denotes a two-dimensional smooth surface in $\mathbb{R}^n$. The unit disk on the xy plane in $\mathbb{R}^2$, for example, consisting of all the points whose distance from the origin is less than or equal to 1. Or a parameterised surface such as the top half of a unit radius sphere in $\mathbb{R}^3$.

- The symbol ∂ (when not being used for partial derivatives) denotes a boundary. So the boundary of a surface S (if it has one) is ∂S. The boundary of an n-dimensional manifold, assuming one exists, is itself a manifold of dimension $n-1$. For example, the boundary ∂S of the top half of a (two dimensional) unit radius sphere S is a (one dimensional) unit radius circle.

- The letter M denotes a space of any dimension (not just one, two or three). The boundary of M (if it has one) is ∂M. So if M is a solid ball in $\mathbb{R}^3$, its boundary, ∂M, is a sphere.

We'll be meeting other types of manifold as we progress, but for now that's enough to be going on with.

A quick word about coordinates. We'll mainly be using Cartesian or rectangular coordinates x, y, z to describe $\mathbb{R}^3$. Sometimes we'll use general coordinates u, v, w or $u^1, u^2, u^3, \ldots, u^n$ or $x^1, x^2, x^3, \ldots, x^n$. To avoid confusion – the context should make the meaning clear – remember the superscripts $1, 2, 3$, etc are coordinate indices, not exponents, so x^2 represents the second coordinate, not x squared. For example, using spherical coordinates r, θ, ϕ we would write

$$x^1 = r,$$

$$x^2 = \theta,$$

$$x^3 = \phi.$$

In n-dimensional space we can write x^i, where i represents any of the coordinate indices $1, 2, 3, \ldots, n$.

1.2 Vectors

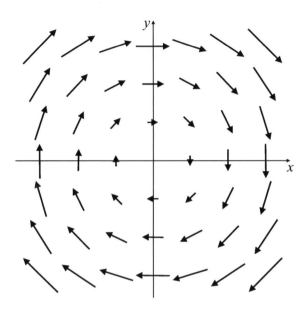

Figure 1.1: Vector field $\mathbf{v}\left(x,y\right)=y\hat{\mathbf{e}}_x-x\hat{\mathbf{e}}_y$.

Vectors will usually be denoted by lower case upright boldface type ($\mathbf{u}$, $\mathbf{v}$, etc). Sometimes we'll number them ($\mathbf{v}_1, \mathbf{v}_2$, etc).

If a vector $\mathbf{v}$ has components v^1, v^2, v^3, we'll write $\mathbf{v}=\left(v^1,v^2,v^3\right).$

In $\mathbb{R}^n$ a vector can be written as a linear combination of the orthogonal standard basis vectors

$$\mathbf{e}_1 = (1,0,\ldots,0,0)\,, \mathbf{e}_2 = (0,1,\ldots,0,0)\,,\ldots, \mathbf{e}_n = (0,0,\ldots,0,1) \qquad (1.2.1)$$

pointing along the $x^1, x^2, \ldots, x^n$ axes. So, for example, a vector in $\mathbb{R}^4$ (four-dimensional Euclidean space) can be written as

$$\mathbf{v} = v^1\mathbf{e}_1 + v^2\mathbf{e}_2 + v^3\mathbf{e}_3 + v^4\mathbf{e}_4,$$

which, using index notation (where i takes the value of $1,2,3$ or 4), can be shortened to $\mathbf{v} = v^i\mathbf{e}_i$.[1]

When using a Cartesian coordinate system, we'll use the conventional notation $\hat{\mathbf{e}}_x, \hat{\mathbf{e}}_y, \hat{\mathbf{e}}_z$ for the standard unit basis vectors pointing along the x, y, z coordinate axes.

---

[1] We are here using the Einstein summation convention, meaning that if a single term contains the same upper and lower index (i in this case), a sum is implied.

A vector field associates a vector to each point in a space. A wind map, for example, indicating wind speed and direction for different points on the Earth's surface. Figure 1.1 shows a plot of the $\mathbb{R}^2$ vector field $\mathbf{v}(x,y) = y\hat{\mathbf{e}}_x - x\hat{\mathbf{e}}_y$. The general form of a three-dimensional vector field in Cartesian coordinates is

$$\mathbf{v}(x,y,z) = f_1(x,y,z)\,\hat{\mathbf{e}}_x + f_2(x,y,z)\,\hat{\mathbf{e}}_y + f_3(x,y,z)\,\hat{\mathbf{e}}_z, \qquad (1.2.2)$$

where the components of the vector at any point are given by the smooth (ie differentiable) scalar functions $f_1(x,y,z)$, $f_2(x,y,z)$ and $f_3(x,y,z)$. Or, more simply, we can write (1.2.2) as

$$\mathbf{v}(x,y,z) = f_1\hat{\mathbf{e}}_x + f_2\hat{\mathbf{e}}_y + f_3\hat{\mathbf{e}}_z.$$

1.3 Tangent vectors

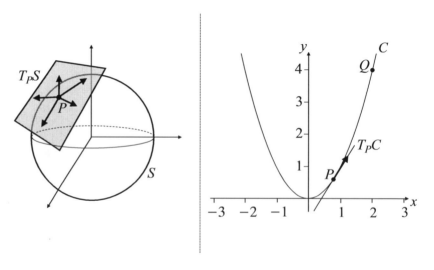

Figure 1.2: Tangent space to sphere and curve.

A vector field on a manifold is constructed by assigning a tangent vector to every point. Intuitively, we can regard a tangent vector as a vector that, at a given point, is tangent to a curve, surface or higher dimensional space. The set of tangent vectors at a point P is a vector space[2] that is called the tangent space $T_P M$ of the manifold M

---

[2] A vector space V is a group of objects (called vectors) that (a) include a zero vector, (b) include an inverse vector, and (c) can be added together, and multiplied by numbers according to a specific set of rules (the vector space axioms). The result of these operations is another member of V. $\mathbb{R}^n$, for example, is a vector space. Consider the Euclidean plane $\mathbb{R}^2$, where a vector is defined as a pair of real numbers (x,y). If we add two vectors (x^1,y^1) and (x^2,y^2), we get another pair of real numbers $(x^1 + x^2, y^1 + y^2)$, ie another vector. And if we multiply a vector (x,y) by a scalar (ie a number) k we get (kx,ky), which is also a vector. A basis for V is a set of linearly

at P. $T_P M$ has the same dimension as M. A tangent space $T_P M$ is attached to every point on M.

In Figure 1.2, the tangent vectors at point P on the surface of a sphere S (embedded in $\mathbb{R}^3$) lie in a plane – the tangent space $T_P S$ – that is tangent to the sphere at P. Also shown is the curve C (embedded in $\mathbb{R}^2$) of $y = f(x) = x^2$. The line tangent to the curve at point P is the tangent space $T_P C$ to the curve at P, ie $T_P C$ is home to all the tangent vectors at P. One way to parameterise C would be with $x = t$ and $y = t^2$. If point $Q(x, y) = (2, 4)$, the tangent vector $\mathbf{v}(t)$ at $T_{(2,4)} C$ is then

$$\mathbf{v} = \frac{dx}{dt}\hat{\mathbf{e}}_x + \frac{dy}{dt}\hat{\mathbf{e}}_y = \hat{\mathbf{e}}_x + 2t\hat{\mathbf{e}}_y$$

$$= \hat{\mathbf{e}}_x + 4\hat{\mathbf{e}}_y.$$

Or, in component form, $\mathbf{v} = (1, 4)$. Different parameterisations of C would give different tangent vectors. For example, we could use $x = 3t$ and $y = 9t^2$, or $x = 10t$ and $y = 100t^2$. However, at point $(2, 4)$ the resulting tangent vectors would all be multiples of $\mathbf{v} = \hat{\mathbf{e}}_x + 4\hat{\mathbf{e}}_y$.

The sphere S and curve C shown in Figure 1.2 are both embedded in Euclidean space, as are their respective tangent spaces $T_P S$ (a plane) and $T_P C$ (a straight line). This notion of embedded manifolds and tangent spaces can be extended to higher dimensions. For example, a three-dimensional manifold M embedded in $\mathbb{R}^4$ would, at a point P, have a tangent space – a hyperplane – also embedded in $\mathbb{R}^4$ and consisting of all the vectors tangent to M at P.

For a more general manifold M that isn't embedded in some $\mathbb{R}^n$, a tangent vector at point P may still be regarded as a vector tangent to a smooth curve that passes through P. However, these 'intrinsic' tangent vectors (think of them as infinitesimally tiny arrows with their base points attached to P) are defined to live *on the manifold M itself*, not embedded in some higher dimensional space. The tangent space $T_P M$ then consists of the set of vectors at P tangent to all smooth curves passing through P.

- Differential forms and tangent vectors live on manifolds. Differential forms and tangent vectors act on each other (at a point, to give a number). Therefore, in this book most of the vectors we discuss are tangent vectors, even if we don't explicitly refer to them as such. Mathematicians have devised various precise but equivalent definitions of tangent vectors on manifolds that, at our level, we don't need to worry about. The essential point is that differential forms act on tangent vectors.

1.4 Parameterisation

It is often convenient to describe manifolds parametrically. A curve can be parameterised using a single parameter. For example, a helix in $\mathbb{R}^3$ has the parametric

---

independent vectors that spans V, meaning any vector in V can be written in terms of the basis vectors. The number of vectors in a basis for V is called the dimension of V. Vector spaces are ubiquitous in mathematics and physics.

equations (with parameter t) $x = \cos t$, $y = \sin t$, $z = t$, which we can also write as a vector equation, using the Greek letter Phi ($\boldsymbol{\Phi}$), as

$$\boldsymbol{\Phi}(t) = \cos t \hat{\mathbf{e}}_x + \sin t \hat{\mathbf{e}}_y + t \hat{\mathbf{e}}_z.$$

Or, in component form:

$$\boldsymbol{\Phi}(t) = (\cos t, \sin t, t).$$

A surface can be parameterised using two parameters. The top half of a unit radius sphere in $\mathbb{R}^3$, for example, can be parameterised (with parameters u and v) by $x = v \cos u$, $y = v \sin u$, $z = \sqrt{1 - v^2}$ for $0 \le u \le 2\pi$, $0 \le v \le 1$. We can write this as the vector equation

$$\boldsymbol{\Phi}(u, v) = v \cos u \hat{\mathbf{e}}_x + v \sin u \hat{\mathbf{e}}_y + \sqrt{1 - v^2} \hat{\mathbf{e}}_z.$$

Or, in component form:

$$\boldsymbol{\Phi}(u, v) = \left(v \cos u, v \sin u, \sqrt{1 - v^2} \right).$$

1.5 Notation for forms

Differential forms will usually be denoted by lower case Greek letters (ω, ν, etc).

Sometimes we'll number them ($\omega_1, \omega_2, \omega_3$, etc).

We'll denote a 1-form ω acting on a vector $\mathbf{v}$ as $\omega(\mathbf{v})$. A 2-form ω acting on two vectors $\mathbf{u}$ and $\mathbf{v}$ will be shown as $\omega(\mathbf{u}, \mathbf{v})$, and so on.

1.6 Cross product

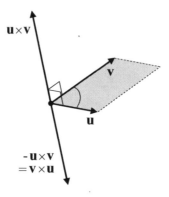

Figure 1.3: Cross product of vectors $\mathbf{u}$ and $\mathbf{v}$.

The cross product $\mathbf{u} \times \mathbf{v}$ of two three-dimensional vectors $\mathbf{u}$ and $\mathbf{v}$ is itself a vector (actually, a pseudovector, but we don't need to worry about that) and is perpendicular to $\mathbf{u}$ and $\mathbf{v}$, as shown in Figure 1.3. By convention the direction of $\mathbf{u} \times \mathbf{v}$ is given by the right-hand rule. Hold the thumb, index finger and second finger of your right hand perpendicular to each other. If your index finger points in the direction of $\mathbf{u}$ and your second finger points in the direction of $\mathbf{v}$, then your thumb points in the direction of $\mathbf{u} \times \mathbf{v}$. The cross product $\mathbf{v} \times \mathbf{u} = -\mathbf{u} \times \mathbf{v}$ is in the opposite direction to $\mathbf{u} \times \mathbf{v}$.

If $\mathbf{u} = u^1\hat{\mathbf{e}}_x + u^2\hat{\mathbf{e}}_y + u^3\hat{\mathbf{e}}_z$ and $\mathbf{v} = v^1\hat{\mathbf{e}}_x + v^2\hat{\mathbf{e}}_y + v^3\hat{\mathbf{e}}_z$, the cross product of $\mathbf{u}$ and $\mathbf{v}$ is given by

$$\mathbf{u} \times \mathbf{v} = \left(u^2v^3 - u^3v^2\right)\hat{\mathbf{e}}_x + \left(u^3v^1 - u^1v^3\right)\hat{\mathbf{e}}_y + \left(u^1v^2 - u^2v^1\right)\hat{\mathbf{e}}_z. \tag{1.6.1}$$

Or, as a 3×3 determinant (see section 1.7),

$$\mathbf{u} \times \mathbf{v} = \begin{vmatrix} \mathbf{i} & \mathbf{j} & \mathbf{k} \\ u^1 & u^2 & u^3 \\ v^1 & v^2 & v^3 \end{vmatrix}. \tag{1.6.2}$$

The area of the parallelogram spanned by $\mathbf{u}$ and $\mathbf{v}$ is given by the magnitude of the cross product $\|\mathbf{u} \times \mathbf{v}\|$.

1.7 Determinants

The determinant is a single number that can be calculated from a square matrix. The determinant has all sorts of weird and wonderful properties, but its importance as far as we're concerned is that it allows us to carry out calculations involving the wedge product. As we'll see, determinants are alternating multilinear functions of their columns (or rows). Being alternating and multilinear are the two key properties of determinants that transfer over to differential forms.

The determinant of a matrix A is denoted by $\det(A)$ or $|A|$.

1.7.1 The determinant of a 1×1 matrix

For a matrix

$$A = [a],$$

the determinant is simply equal to a, ie

$$|A| = a.$$

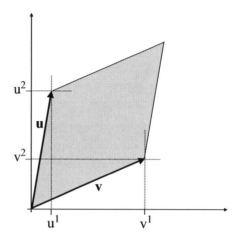

Figure 1.4: Parallelogram spanned by **u** and **v**.

1.7.2 The determinant of a 2×2 matrix

For a matrix

$$A = \begin{bmatrix} a & b \\ c & d \end{bmatrix},$$

the determinant is given by

$$|A| = ad - cb.$$

Figure 1.4 shows a parallelogram spanned by two vectors: $\mathbf{u} = u^1 \hat{\mathbf{e}}_x + u^2 \hat{\mathbf{e}}_y$ and $\mathbf{v} = v^1 \hat{\mathbf{e}}_x + v^2 \hat{\mathbf{e}}_y$. If we write **u** and **v** as column vectors, we get the matrix

$$\begin{bmatrix} u^1 & v^1 \\ u^2 & v^2 \end{bmatrix}.$$

The determinant of this matrix gives the area of the spanned parallelogram:

$$\begin{vmatrix} u^1 & v^1 \\ u^2 & v^2 \end{vmatrix} = u^1 v^2 - u^2 v^1.$$

Determinants are alternating, which means if we interchange any two columns (or rows), the determinant changes sign. So if we swap the vectors, we swap the sign of the area, ie

$$\begin{vmatrix} v^1 & u^1 \\ v^2 & u^2 \end{vmatrix} = v^1 u^2 - v^2 u^1.$$

So we say the determinant gives the *signed* area of the spanned parallelogram. We'll revisit this notion of things being alternating – the sign changing when the order of the vectors is flipped – when we see how 2-forms and higher degree forms act on vectors to spit out a number. The number will be positive or negative depending on the order that we feed the vectors to the differential form.

Determinants are also multilinear in terms of their columns (or rows). This means if we multiply the vector $\mathbf{u} = \left(u^1, u^2\right)$ by a constant k, the resulting determinant

$$\begin{vmatrix} ku^1 & v^1 \\ ku^2 & v^2 \end{vmatrix} = k\left(u^1 v^2 - u^2 v^1\right)$$

is k times the size of the original determinant $u^1 v^2 - u^2 v^1$.

1.7.3 The determinant of a 3×3 matrix

For a matrix

$$A = \begin{bmatrix} a & b & c \\ d & e & f \\ g & h & i \end{bmatrix},$$

the determinant is given by

$$|A| = a\left(ei - fh\right) - b\left(di - fg\right) + c\left(dh - eg\right),$$

which is equivalent to

$$|A| = a\begin{vmatrix} e & f \\ h & i \end{vmatrix} - b\begin{vmatrix} d & f \\ g & i \end{vmatrix} + c\begin{vmatrix} d & e \\ g & h \end{vmatrix}.$$

There are alternative forms, including

$$|A| = a\left(ei - fh\right) + b\left(fg - di\right) + c\left(dh - eg\right). \tag{1.7.1}$$

The volume of a parallelepiped spanned by three vectors, $\mathbf{u} = u^1\hat{\mathbf{e}}_x + u^2\hat{\mathbf{e}}_y + u^3\hat{\mathbf{e}}_z$, $\mathbf{v} = v^1\hat{\mathbf{e}}_x + v^2\hat{\mathbf{e}}_y + v^3\hat{\mathbf{e}}_z$ and $\mathbf{w} = w^1\hat{\mathbf{e}}_x + w^2\hat{\mathbf{e}}_y + w^3\hat{\mathbf{e}}_z$, as shown in Figure 1.5, is the determinant of the column vector matrix

$$\begin{bmatrix} u^1 & v^1 & w^1 \\ u^2 & v^2 & w^2 \\ u^3 & v^3 & w^3 \end{bmatrix}.$$

This is a signed volume because if we swap any two column vectors, the sign of the determinant changes.

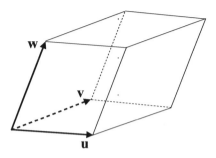

Figure 1.5: Parallelepiped spanned by $\mathbf{u}, \mathbf{v}$ and $\mathbf{w}$.

1.7.4 The determinant of an $n \times n$ matrix, where $n > 3$

Tricky to visualise, trickier to draw, a parallelotope is a generalization of the two-dimensional parallelogram and three-dimensional parallelepiped into higher dimension. The determinant of an $n \times n$ matrix, where $n > 3$, gives the signed volume of the n-dimensional parallelotope spanned by the matrix's n column vectors.

Example 1.1. In $\mathbb{R}^4$, find the volume of the parallelotope spanned by the vectors $\mathbf{v}_1 = (3,0,0,0)$, $\mathbf{v}_2 = (0,3,0,0)$, $\mathbf{v}_3 = (0,0,3,0)$ and $\mathbf{v}_4 = (0,0,0,3)$.

This parallelotope is actually a four-dimensional cube of side length 3, so the volume equals $3^4 = 81$. The volume is also given by the determinant of the column vector matrix

$$\begin{bmatrix} 3 & 0 & 0 & 0 \\ 0 & 3 & 0 & 0 \\ 0 & 0 & 3 & 0 \\ 0 & 0 & 0 & 3 \end{bmatrix} = 81.$$

You can check this result using the WolframAlpha online calculator [22] by typing the following into the input box and hitting Enter:

```
determinant {{3,0,0,0},{0,3,0,0},{0,0,3,0},{0,0,0,3}}
```

It's easy enough to check this is a signed volume by swapping any two column vectors and seeing that the sign of the determinant changes.

2 What are differential forms?

Differential forms are linear or, more generally, multilinear alternating functions of tangent vectors.

- A 0-form is a special case and is simply a smooth function. A 0-forms eats a point and returns a number.

- A 1-form eats a vector and returns a number.

- A 2-form eats two vectors and returns a number.

- A 3-form eats three vectors and returns a number.

- A k-form eats k vectors and returns a number.

In terms of identification, differential forms can be generally recognised as things containing differentials such as dx, dy and dz. So these are 1-forms (each term contains one differential)

$$\omega = 2x\,dx + 3y\,dy - dz,$$

$$\omega = x\,dy,$$

$$\omega = dx.$$

This is a 2-form

$$\omega = 8\,dy \wedge dz,$$

and this is a 3-form

$$\omega = -7z\,dx \wedge dy \wedge dz,$$

where the $\wedge$ symbol denotes a type of multiplication called the wedge product (details to follow).

A vector field on a manifold gives a vector (actually, a tangent vector) at every point. So, for example, say a point P on M, a region of $\mathbb{R}^3$, has coordinates $x = 3, y = 5, z = 1$. At P the vector field

$$\mathbf{v} = 7x\hat{\mathbf{e}}_x + 4y\hat{\mathbf{e}}_y + 2\hat{\mathbf{e}}_z$$

gives the (tangent) vector

$$\mathbf{v} = (7 \times 3)\,\hat{\mathbf{e}}_x + (4 \times 5)\,\hat{\mathbf{e}}_y + 2\hat{\mathbf{e}}_z$$

$$\mathbf{v} = 21\hat{\mathbf{e}}_x + 20\hat{\mathbf{e}}_y + 2\hat{\mathbf{e}}_z.$$

Similarly, a differential form on a manifold can be thought of as a differential form *field*, that gives a particular differential form at every point. For example, at the same point $P\,(3,5,1)$ on M the above 1-form *field*, $\omega = 2x\,dx + 3y\,dy - dz$, gives the particular 1-form

$$\omega = (2 \times 3)\,dx + (3 \times 5)\,dy - dz$$

$$\omega = 6\,dx + 15\,dy - dz.$$

As we'll see, if the tangent vector and 1-form are associated with the same point, they can act on each other to give a number.

Following widely accepted practice, we won't use the term 'field', as in 'differential form field'. Instead, we'll let 'differential form' refer to both a differential form at a point *and* a differential form field on the manifold.

(A hint of what is to come: just as the vectors $\hat{\mathbf{e}}_x, \hat{\mathbf{e}}_y$ and $\hat{\mathbf{e}}_z$ form a set of basis vectors for $\mathbb{R}^3$, the differentials dx, dy and dz form a set of basis 1-forms for $\mathbb{R}^3$.)

2.1 0-forms

A 0-form is simply a smooth scalar function. For example:

$$f\,(x,y,z) = x^2 - zy,$$

which takes a point on a manifold, in this case $\mathbb{R}^3$, and returns a number.

2.2 1-forms

At a point, a 1-form takes a tangent vector and returns a number. In maths-speak, a 1-form is a function that requires one vector argument. Not only that, a 1-form ω is a *linear* real-valued function of vectors, in the sense of

$$\omega\,(a\mathbf{u} + b\mathbf{v}) = a\omega\,(\mathbf{u}) + b\omega\,(\mathbf{v}),$$

where a and b are real numbers.

On $\mathbb{R}^3$ a 1-form will include one or more of the differentials dx, dy, dz and look something like

$$\omega = f_1\,(x,y,z)\,dx + f_2\,(x,y,z)\,dy + f_3\,(x,y,z)\,dz,$$

where $f_i\,(x,y,z)$ are smooth scalar functions. Or, more simply, we can write

$$\omega = f_1\,dx + f_2\,dy + f_3\,dz.$$

(Later on, we'll explore the reasons for this dx, dy, dz notation). Of course, we're not limited to Cartesian coordinates in three dimensions. In general coordinates $x^1, x^2, x^3, \ldots, x^n$, a 1-form would be written as

$$\omega = f_1 \, dx^1 + f_2 \, dx^2 + \ldots + f_n \, dx^n,$$

where f_i are smooth functions of $x^1, x^2, x^3, \ldots, x^n$.

The differential of a smooth function $f(x, y, z)$ is

$$df = \frac{\partial f}{\partial x} dx + \frac{\partial f}{\partial y} dy + \frac{\partial f}{\partial z} dz, \qquad (2.2.1)$$

and is a 1-form. So the differential of the function

$$f(x, y, z) = xz + 4y^3 + 3xy$$

is the 1-form

$$df = (3y + z) \, dx + \left(3x + 12y^2\right) dy + x \, dz.$$

Even the most humble little dx can be regarded as the differential of a function. Suppose we want to change from using x, y, z coordinates to some other u, v, w coordinate system. If the old x, y, z coordinates are functions of the new u, v, w coordinates we can find the differential of $x(u, v, w)$, which is

$$dx = \frac{\partial x}{\partial u} du + \frac{\partial x}{\partial v} dv + \frac{\partial x}{\partial w} dw,$$

and so on for dy and dz.

Not all 1-forms are the differentials of functions. For example, there is no function whose differential is the perfectly acceptable 1-form

$$\omega = x \, dx + x \, dy.$$

Another way of looking at differential forms is simply as objects that can be integrated, including the differential. So in this integral:

$$\int_a^b \underbrace{6x \, dx}_{\text{1-form}},$$

$6x \, dx$ is a 1-form.

Because we can combine like differentials, we can add two 1-forms together to get another 1-form. For example, we can add $5 \, dx$ and $3x \, dx + 8 \, dy$ to get $(3x + 5) \, dx + 8 \, dy$.

27

2.2.1 The meaning of dx^i

When we first learned calculus we were taught that df in the aforementioned (2.2.1) differential of a function $f(x, y, z)$,

$$df = \frac{\partial f}{\partial x}dx + \frac{\partial f}{\partial y}dy + \frac{\partial f}{\partial z}dz,$$

represented an infinitesimal change in f associated with infinitesimal changes dx, dy, dz (collectively referred to, using index notation, as dx^i) of the x, y, z coordinates.

However, at the start of this chapter we referred to the *1-form* $\omega = dx$. What's the justification for that? Why change a perfectly reasonable (so we were told) infinitesimal change into a more complicated object called a 1-form?

The first thing to point out is that, in terms of doing practical calculus calculations, there's nothing wrong with the traditional treatment of dx^i as infinitesimals. It does turn out, though, that mathematicians aren't too happy talking about infinitely small changes; they see the notion as being a bit sloppy. The modern way of interpreting dx^i is as functions of tangent vectors, ie as 1-forms. Spivak [21] explains:

> Classical differential geometers (and classical analysts) did not hesitate to talk about 'infinitely small' changes dx^i of the coordinates x^i, just as Leibniz had. No one wanted to admit that this was nonsense, because true results were obtained when these infinitely small quantities were divided into each other (provided one did it in the right way).

> Eventually it was realized that the closest one can come to describing an infinitely small change is to describe a direction in which this change is supposed to occur, ie a tangent vector. Since df is supposed to be the infinitesimal change of f under an infinitesimal change of the point, df must be a function of this change, which means that df should be a function on tangent vectors. The dx^i themselves then metamorphosed into functions ...

The old notation still works, we can still use it, but the underlying machinery has been changed and made more mathematically rigorous. We'll be taking a closer look at the infinitesimal vs 1-form view of differentials later in this chapter. Our essential takeaway for now is that, depending on context, we can regard the differentials dx^i *either* as infinitesimals or 1-forms.

2.2.2 How this works – basis 1-forms and basis vectors

So how do differential forms eat tangent vectors and spit out numbers? The answer lies in the relationship between basis vectors and basis 1-forms. Here's a vector:

$$\mathbf{v} = 3\hat{\mathbf{e}}_x - \hat{\mathbf{e}}_y + 6\hat{\mathbf{e}}_z, \tag{2.2.2}$$

with the standard unit basis vectors $\hat{\mathbf{e}}_x, \hat{\mathbf{e}}_y, \hat{\mathbf{e}}_z$.

And here's a 1-form:

$$\omega = 5\,dx + 2\,dy + 4\,dz, \tag{2.2.3}$$

where dx, dy and dz are the corresponding set of basis 1-forms. We say 'corresponding' because the basis vectors we choose induce a unique 1-form basis. (Or vice versa: a set of basis 1-forms will induce a unique set of basis vectors.) Mathematicians are able to define these bases so they act on each other as follows (we'll explore the reasons behind this definition later in this chapter):

$$dx\,(\hat{\mathbf{e}}_x) = 1, \quad dx\,(\hat{\mathbf{e}}_y) = 0, \quad dx\,(\hat{\mathbf{e}}_z) = 0, \tag{2.2.4}$$

$$dy\,(\hat{\mathbf{e}}_x) = 0, \quad dy\,(\hat{\mathbf{e}}_y) = 1, \quad dy\,(\hat{\mathbf{e}}_z) = 0,$$

$$dz\,(\hat{\mathbf{e}}_x) = 0, \quad dz\,(\hat{\mathbf{e}}_y) = 0, \quad dz\,(\hat{\mathbf{e}}_z) = 1.$$

The basis vectors and basis 1-forms are said to be dual to each other – one acts on the other to produce either 1 or 0. If you're familiar with the Kronecker delta and index notation, this dual relationship can be succinctly written as

$$dx^i\,(\mathbf{e}_j) = \delta^i_j = \left\{ \begin{array}{l} 1 \ \text{if}\, i = j \\ 0 \ \text{if}\, i \neq j \end{array} \right. .$$

So, at a point, when the 1-form (2.2.3) acts on the vector (2.2.2) we can write

$$\omega\,(\mathbf{v}) = (5\,dx + 2\,dy + 4\,dz)\,(3\hat{\mathbf{e}}_x - \hat{\mathbf{e}}_y + 6\hat{\mathbf{e}}_z)$$

$$= (5 \times 3) + (2 \times -1) + (4 \times 6)$$

$$= 37.$$

Effectively, we're multiplying the 1-form components by the respective vector components, ie the 1-form $\omega = a\,dx + b\,dy + c\,dz$ acts on a vector $\mathbf{v} = d\hat{\mathbf{e}}_x + e\hat{\mathbf{e}}_y + f\hat{\mathbf{e}}_z$ as:

$$\omega\,(\mathbf{v}) = ad + be + cf,$$

which, of course, is a number. Using index notation, we write

$$\omega\,(\mathbf{v}) = \omega_i v^i.$$

We won't go there, but using the coordinate transformation rules for 1-forms and tangent vectors (also known as the covariant and contravariant transformation rules) it is straightforward to show that:

- $\omega\,(\mathbf{v})$ is an invariant quantity.

If we used those rules to change to a different coordinate system, spherical coordinates (r, θ, ϕ), for example, $\omega = 5\,dx + 2\,dy + 4\,dz$ and $\mathbf{v} = 3\hat{\mathbf{e}}_x - \hat{\mathbf{e}}_y + 6\hat{\mathbf{e}}_z$ would have different components and different bases but $\omega\,(\mathbf{v})$ would still be 37.

We mentioned in section 1.2 that the set of tangent vectors at a point P is a vector space called the tangent space $T_P M$ of the manifold M at P. The set of 1-forms at P

is also a vector space (of the same dimension as $T_P M$ and M) that goes by the name of the cotangent space $T_P^* M$ at P. In maths-speak, $T_P^* M$ is defined to be the dual space of $T_P M$, meaning the basis vectors from $T_P M$ and basis 1-forms from $T_P^* M$ act on each other as described above to give either 1 or 0.

- In other words, 1-forms are functions on the tangent space, ie they have a domain (the set of their possible input values) of $T_P M$ and a range (the set of their possible outputs) of the real numbers. Using slightly more advanced mathematical language, this dual relationship can be written as

$$\omega_P : T_P M \to \mathbb{R},$$

meaning ω_P (an element of the cotangent space $T_P^* M$, ie a 1-form) acts on an element of the tangent space $T_P M$ (ie a tangent vector) to give a real number. Similarly, k-forms (where $k > 1$) have a domain of multiple copies of $T_P M$ and, again, a range of the real numbers.

2.2.3 dx^i picks out a vector's ith component

If the basis 1-form dx acts, at a point, on the vector $\mathbf{v} = 3\hat{\mathbf{e}}_x - \hat{\mathbf{e}}_y + 6\hat{\mathbf{e}}_z$ it picks out the vector's $\hat{\mathbf{e}}_x$ component, which in this case is 3:

$$\omega\left(\mathbf{v}\right) = dx\left(3\hat{\mathbf{e}}_x - \hat{\mathbf{e}}_y + 6\hat{\mathbf{e}}_z\right)$$

$$= \left(1 \times 3\right) - 0 + 0$$

$$= 3,$$

because $dx\left(\hat{\mathbf{e}}_x\right) = 1$, $dx\left(\hat{\mathbf{e}}_y\right) = 0$ and $dx\left(\hat{\mathbf{e}}_z\right) = 0$.

Using index notation we can say

$$dx^i\left(\mathbf{v}\right) = v^i. \tag{2.2.5}$$

In other words, dx^i picks out the ith component of a vector $\mathbf{v}$.

Geometrically, we can interpret (2.2.5) as giving the projection of $\mathbf{v}$ onto the x^ith coordinate axis. So $dx\left(\mathbf{v}\right) = 3$ gives the projection of $\mathbf{v}$ onto the x axis; $dy\left(\mathbf{v}\right) = -1$ gives the projection of $\mathbf{v}$ onto the y axis; and $dz\left(\mathbf{v}\right) = 6$ gives the projection of $\mathbf{v}$ onto the z axis. If we let $a\,dx$ (where a is a constant) act on $\mathbf{v}$, $a\,dx\left(\mathbf{v}\right) = 3a$ gives the projection of $\mathbf{v}$ onto the x axis multiplied by the factor a.

In a small abuse of notation, we may omit the basis vectors and write

$$dx\left(3, -1, 6\right) = 3,$$

or, for dy acting on vector $\mathbf{w} = 12\hat{\mathbf{e}}_x + 7\hat{\mathbf{e}}_y + 1\hat{\mathbf{e}}_z$,

$$dy\left(12, 7, 1\right) = 7.$$

2.2.4 An example using polar coordinates

2.2.4.1 Calculating the basis vectors and 1-forms

Let's see how this works in polar coordinates. We'll start by calculating the polar basis vectors $\mathbf{e}_r, \mathbf{e}_\theta$ and the polar basis 1-forms $dr, d\theta$, and then show that when they act on each other the result is either 1 or 0. In other words, we want to show:

$$dr\left(\mathbf{e}_r\right) = 1,$$

$$d\theta\left(\mathbf{e}_\theta\right) = 1,$$

$$dr\left(\mathbf{e}_\theta\right) = 0,$$

$$d\theta\left(\mathbf{e}_r\right) = 0.$$

First, the basis vectors. In order to proceed, we need the formula for how Cartesian basis vectors transform to polar basis vectors (which we'll derive in section 2.2.6.2). For now, here it is:

$$\left(\mathbf{e}_r, \mathbf{e}_\theta\right) = \left(\hat{\mathbf{e}}_x, \hat{\mathbf{e}}_y\right) \begin{bmatrix} \frac{\partial x}{\partial r} & \frac{\partial x}{\partial \theta} \\ \frac{\partial y}{\partial r} & \frac{\partial y}{\partial \theta} \end{bmatrix}. \tag{2.2.6}$$

Multiplying this out we get

$$\left(\mathbf{e}_r, \mathbf{e}_\theta\right) = \left(\frac{\partial x}{\partial r}\hat{\mathbf{e}}_x + \frac{\partial y}{\partial r}\hat{\mathbf{e}}_y, \frac{\partial x}{\partial \theta}\hat{\mathbf{e}}_x + \frac{\partial y}{\partial \theta}\hat{\mathbf{e}}_y\right)$$

In polar coordinates, $x = r\cos\theta$ and $y = r\sin\theta$. And, going the other way, $r = \left(x^2 + y^2\right)^{1/2}$ and $\theta = \arctan\left(y/x\right)$.

The basis vectors are, starting with $\mathbf{e}_r$,

$$\mathbf{e}_r = \frac{\partial x}{\partial r}\hat{\mathbf{e}}_x + \frac{\partial y}{\partial r}\hat{\mathbf{e}}_y$$

$$\mathbf{e}_r = \cos\theta\hat{\mathbf{e}}_x + \sin\theta\hat{\mathbf{e}}_y.$$

And for $\mathbf{e}_\theta$,

$$\mathbf{e}_\theta = \frac{\partial x}{\partial \theta}\hat{\mathbf{e}}_x + \frac{\partial y}{\partial \theta}\hat{\mathbf{e}}_y$$

$$\mathbf{e}_\theta = -r\sin\theta\hat{\mathbf{e}}_x + r\cos\theta\hat{\mathbf{e}}_y.$$

Next, the basis 1-forms. As θ is a function of x and y, we can find the differential $d\theta$ using (2.2.1)

$$df = \frac{\partial f}{\partial x}dx + \frac{\partial f}{\partial y}dy + \frac{\partial f}{\partial z}dz.$$

And we can say

$$d\theta = \frac{\partial \theta}{\partial x}dx + \frac{\partial \theta}{\partial y}dy$$

$$d\theta = -\frac{1}{r}\sin\theta dx + \frac{1}{r}\cos\theta dy.$$

Similarly, for dr

$$dr = \cos\theta dx + \sin\theta dy.$$

We saw above in (2.2.4) how the Cartesian basis vectors and basis 1-forms are dual to each other. The same is true with our newly minted polar basis vectors $\mathbf{e}_r, \mathbf{e}_\theta$ and basis 1-forms $dr, d\theta$:

$$dr\,(\mathbf{e}_r) = (\cos\theta dx + \sin\theta dy)(\cos\theta\hat{\mathbf{e}}_x + \sin\theta\hat{\mathbf{e}}_y) = 1,$$

because $\cos^2\theta + \sin^2\theta = 1$. Similarly

$$d\theta\,(\mathbf{e}_\theta) = \left(-\frac{1}{r}\sin\theta dx + \frac{1}{r}\cos\theta dy\right)(-r\sin\theta\hat{\mathbf{e}}_x + r\cos\theta\hat{\mathbf{e}}_y) = 1,$$

$$dr\,(\mathbf{e}_\theta) = (\cos\theta dx + \sin\theta dy)(-r\sin\theta\hat{\mathbf{e}}_x + r\cos\theta\hat{\mathbf{e}}_y) = 0,$$

$$d\theta\,(\mathbf{e}_r) = \left(-\frac{1}{r}\sin\theta dx + \frac{1}{r}\cos\theta dy\right)(\cos\theta\hat{\mathbf{e}}_x + \sin\theta\hat{\mathbf{e}}_y) = 0.$$

Note that unlike their Cartesian counterparts, the polar basis vectors $\mathbf{e}_r, \mathbf{e}_\theta$ and basis 1-forms $dr, d\theta$ change from one point to another.

We can also easily verify that although $\mathbf{e}_r$ is a unit vector, $\mathbf{e}_\theta$ is not. To show this, we change $\mathbf{e}_r, \mathbf{e}_\theta$ to polar unit vectors $\hat{\mathbf{e}}_r, \hat{\mathbf{e}}_\theta$ by dividing by their magnitudes:

$$\hat{\mathbf{e}}_r = \frac{\mathbf{e}_r}{\|\mathbf{e}_r\|} = \frac{\cos\theta\hat{\mathbf{e}}_x + \sin\theta\hat{\mathbf{e}}_y}{\|\cos\theta\hat{\mathbf{e}}_x + \sin\theta\hat{\mathbf{e}}_y\|} = \frac{\cos\theta\hat{\mathbf{e}}_x + \sin\theta\hat{\mathbf{e}}_y}{\sqrt{\cos^2\theta + \sin^2\theta}}$$

$$= \cos\theta\hat{\mathbf{e}}_x + \sin\theta\hat{\mathbf{e}}_y = \mathbf{e}_r.$$

$$\hat{\mathbf{e}}_\theta = \frac{\mathbf{e}_\theta}{\|\mathbf{e}_\theta\|} = \frac{-r\sin\theta\hat{\mathbf{e}}_x + r\cos\theta\hat{\mathbf{e}}_y}{\|-r\sin\theta\hat{\mathbf{e}}_x + r\cos\theta\hat{\mathbf{e}}_y\|} = \frac{-r\sin\theta\hat{\mathbf{e}}_x + r\cos\theta\hat{\mathbf{e}}_y}{r\left(\sqrt{\sin^2\theta + \cos^2\theta}\right)}$$

$$= -\sin\theta\hat{\mathbf{e}}_x + \cos\theta\hat{\mathbf{e}}_y = \frac{\mathbf{e}_\theta}{r} \neq \mathbf{e}_\theta.$$

2.2.4.2 Tangent vectors to a circle

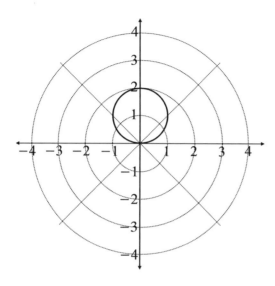

Figure 2.1: Graph of $r = 2\sin\theta$.

Recall (2.2.5)

$$dx^i(\mathbf{v}) = v^i,$$

which tells us that dx^i picks out the ith component of vector $\mathbf{v}$. So, for example, $i = 1 \to dx^1$ would pick out a vector's first component, and $i = 2 \to dx^2$ would pick out a vector's second component. (Remember, the superscripts 1 and 2 are coordinate indices, *not* exponents.) Let's now try this in polar coordinates with tangent vectors to a circle. We'll pick out the first and second components of tangent vector $\mathbf{v}(t)$ using $dx^1 = dr$ and $dx^2 = d\theta$. Again, we'll be making use of the Pythagorean identity $\cos^2\theta + \sin^2\theta = 1$.

Figure 2.1 shows the polar graph of the circle $r = 2\sin\theta$. We can parameterise this circle by letting $\theta = t$ and $r = 2\sin t$ for $0 \le t \le \pi$. A tangent vector $\mathbf{v}(t)$ to the circle is then given by

$$\mathbf{v} = \frac{dr}{dt}\mathbf{e}_r + \frac{d\theta}{dt}\mathbf{e}_\theta$$

$$\mathbf{v} = (2\cos t)\,\mathbf{e}_r + 1\mathbf{e}_\theta.$$

Or, in component form, $\mathbf{v} = (2\cos t, 1)$.

Substituting the previously calculated equations for $\mathbf{e}_r$ and $\mathbf{e}_\theta$ gives

$$\mathbf{v} = 2\cos t \left(\cos\theta\hat{\mathbf{e}}_x + \sin\theta\hat{\mathbf{e}}_y\right) + 1 \times \left(-r\sin\theta\hat{\mathbf{e}}_x + r\cos\theta\hat{\mathbf{e}}_y\right).$$

Now apply $dx^1 = dr = \cos\theta dx + \sin\theta dy$

$$dr\left(\mathbf{v}\right) = \left(\cos\theta dx + \sin\theta dy\right)\left(2\cos t\left(\cos\theta\hat{\mathbf{e}}_x + \sin\theta\hat{\mathbf{e}}_y\right) + \left(-r\sin\theta\hat{\mathbf{e}}_x + r\cos\theta\hat{\mathbf{e}}_y\right)\right)$$

$$= 2\cos t,$$

which is the first component of $\mathbf{v}\left(t\right)$.

Next, apply $dx^2 = d\theta = -\frac{1}{r}\sin\theta dx + \frac{1}{r}\cos\theta dy$

$$dr\left(\mathbf{v}\right) = \left(-\frac{1}{r}\sin\theta dx + \frac{1}{r}\cos\theta dy\right)\left(2\cos t\left(\cos\theta\hat{\mathbf{e}}_x + \sin\theta\hat{\mathbf{e}}_y\right) + \left(-r\sin\theta\hat{\mathbf{e}}_x + r\cos\theta\hat{\mathbf{e}}_y\right)\right)$$

$$= 1,$$

which is the second component of $\mathbf{v}\left(t\right)$.

2.2.5 Curves

A curve is a one-dimensional manifold and can be parameterised by a single parameter, t for example. So in $\mathbb{R}^3$ we might have a curve described by the parametric equation

$$\boldsymbol{\Phi}\left(t\right) = \left(t, 3t^2, 5t\right),$$

which means

$$x = t,\ y = 3t^2,\ z = 5t.$$

The tangent vector along this curve is given by

$$\frac{d\boldsymbol{\Phi}}{dt} = \left(\frac{dx}{dt}, \frac{dy}{dt}, \frac{dz}{dt}\right) = \left(1, 6t, 5\right).$$

We can show a 1-form ω acting on $\frac{d\boldsymbol{\Phi}}{dt}$ by

$$\omega\left(\frac{d\boldsymbol{\Phi}}{dt}\right).$$

Equation (2.2.5)

$$dx^i\left(\mathbf{v}\right) = v^i,$$

tells us that dx^i picks out the ith component of vector $\mathbf{v}$. So if $\omega = dy$, then

$$dy\left(\frac{d\boldsymbol{\Phi}}{dt}\right) = dy\left(\frac{dx}{dt}, \frac{dy}{dt}, \frac{dz}{dt}\right) = dy\left(1, 6t, 5\right) = 6t.$$

2.2.6 The differential df revisited

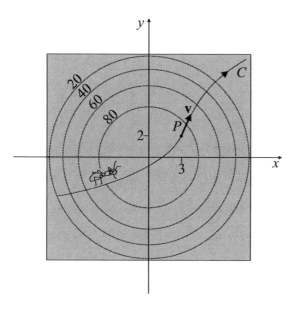

Figure 2.2: Ant on a hotplate.

Say we have a scalar field f on a manifold, ie a function that assigns a scalar (a number) to every point on the manifold. At a given point, the 1-form df acts on a tangent vector $\mathbf{v} = \frac{d\mathbf{\Phi}}{dt}$ to give a number, the directional derivative $df(\mathbf{v})$, which tells us how much f is changing in the direction of $\mathbf{v}$ with respect to t.

For example, consider a heat-resistant ant on a hotplate walking along a curve C, as shown in Figure 2.2. Let's assume the temperature of the hotplate is given by the scalar function $f(x,y) = 100 - (x^2 + y^2)$. In the diagram, contours of constant temperature are shown by broken-line circles. We'll also assume that we can describe the ant's progress along C using some parametric equation $\mathbf{\Phi}(t)$, and that t measures time in minutes. The tangent vector along C is given by

$$\mathbf{v} = \frac{d\mathbf{\Phi}}{dt} = \left(\frac{dx}{dt}, \frac{dy}{dt} \right).$$

As the ant moves along C, the directional derivative $df(\mathbf{v})$ gives the instantaneous rate of temperature change per minute in her direction of travel. So, for example, if at point $P(3,2)$ the tangent vector $\mathbf{v} = (1,2)$, then

$$df(\mathbf{v}) = -(2x\,dx + 2y\,dy)\left(\frac{dx}{dt}, \frac{dy}{dt} \right) = -(6\,dx + 4\,dy)(1,2) = -14.$$

Meaning that at $P(3,2)$ the ant would experience a temperature rate of change with respect to time of -14 temperature units per minute in the direction of $\mathbf{v}$.

2.2.6.1 $df(\mathbf{v})$ as an approximation to Δf

Recall from section 2.2.1 the Spivak [21] quote stating that df should correctly be regarded as a 1-form rather than an infinitesimal change of f. We can now look at this idea a little more closely.

In elementary calculus the differential of a function $f(x,y,z)$ is a scalar (or number)

$$df = \frac{\partial f}{\partial x}dx + \frac{\partial f}{\partial y}dy + \frac{\partial f}{\partial z}dz,$$

representing either an infinitesimal change in f associated with infinitesimal changes dx, dy, dz, or a small change $df \approx \Delta f$ associated with small changes $dx = \Delta x, dy = \Delta y, dz = \Delta z$ in the independent variables x, y, z. So, for example, the above 'hotplate' function $f(x,y) = 100 - (x^2 + y^2)$ gives $df = -(2x\,dx + 2y\,dy)$, which at point $P(3,2)$ gives $df = -(6\,dx + 4\,dy)$. If we change x from 3 to 3.1 and y from 2 to 2.1, we have $dx = \Delta x = 0.1$ and $dy = \Delta y = 0.1$, giving

$$\Delta f = \left(100 - (3.1)^2 - (2.1)^2\right) - \left(100 - 3^2 - 2^2\right) = -1.02,$$

and

$$df = -(6 \times 0.1 + 4 \times 0.1) = -1.$$

If we repeat the exercise with $dx = \Delta x = 0.01$ and $dy = \Delta y = 0.01$, we find $\Delta f = -0.1002$ and $df = -0.1$. And with $dx = \Delta x = 0.001$ and $dy = \Delta y = 0.001$, we find $\Delta f = -0.010002$ and $df = -0.01$. In other words, the smaller we make $dx = \Delta x$ and $dy = \Delta y$, the better is the approximation $\Delta f \approx df$.

The modern interpretation of df is as a 1-form, not a number. In order to change the 1-form df to a number we need to feed it a direction, ie a tangent vector. We can demonstrate this using the same function $f(x,y) = 100 - (x^2 + y^2)$, again at point $P(3,2)$. In effect, we will now repeat the above calculation but with a different interpretation as to the meaning of df. A displacement Δf from P along an ordinary Euclidean vector $\mathbf{v} = (v^1, v^2)$ can be written as

$$\Delta f = f\left(P + (v^1, v^2)\right) - f(P).$$

Now let's input a small vector, $\mathbf{v} = (0.1, 0.1)$, to (again) get

$$\Delta f = f(P(3.1, 2.1)) - f(3,2)$$

$$= \left(100 - (3.1^2 + 2.1^2)\right) - \left(100 - (3^2 + 2^2)\right) = -1.02.$$

Because we are working in $\mathbb{R}^2$ (the xy plane), we can also treat $\mathbf{v}$ as a tangent vector and calculate $df(\mathbf{v})$, which equals

$$df(\mathbf{v}) = -(6\,dx + 4\,dy)(0.1, 0.1) = -1.$$

As with the previous 'df as a number' calculations, the smaller we make $\mathbf{v}$, the better is the approximation $\Delta f \approx df(\mathbf{v})$. By considering df as a 1-form, a linear function that acts on tangent vector, we are thus able to recover the elementary interpretation of df as the small change in f associated with small changes in the independent variables x, y, z.

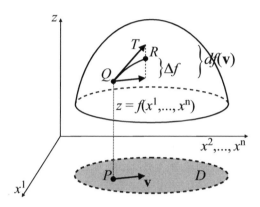

Figure 2.3: The differential as an approximation to Δf.

The general, multidimensional case for a function $z = f\left(x^1, \ldots, x^n,\right)$ is shown in Figure 2.3 (from Lee [12]). In the diagram, D is a region of $\mathbb{R}^n$ with coordinates $x^1, \ldots, x^n$, $\mathbf{v} = \left(v^1, \ldots, v^n\right)$ is a vector in D, and P is a point in D.

As noted above, a displacement Δf from P along $\mathbf{v}$ can be written as

$$\Delta f = f\left(P + \left(v^1, \ldots, v^n\right)\right) - f(P),$$

where $f(P)$ is the value of f at point Q and $f\left(P + \left(v^1, \ldots, v^n\right)\right)$ is the value of f at point R.

In two dimensions, for a function $z = f(x)$, tangent T would be a straight line. In three dimensions, for a function $z = f(x, y)$, T would be a plane. In more than three dimensions, T would be a higher dimensional space. The slope of T is given by the ratio of 'rise' to 'run'. So the 'rise' of T equals slope multiplied by 'run'. The slope of T along the x^1 axis is $\frac{\partial f}{\partial x^1}$, the 'run' is v^1, giving a 'rise' of $\frac{\partial f}{\partial x^1}\left(v^1\right)$. The total 'rise' of T is therefore given by

$$\left(\frac{\partial f}{\partial x^1} + \frac{\partial f}{\partial x^2} + \ldots + \frac{\partial f}{\partial x^n}\right)\left(v^1 + v^2 + \ldots + v^n\right),$$

which we can rewrite, knowing that dx^i picks out the ith component of $\mathbf{v}$, as

$$\left(\frac{\partial f}{\partial x^1}dx^1 + \frac{\partial f}{\partial x^2}dx^2 + \ldots + \frac{\partial f}{\partial x^n}dx^n\right)(\mathbf{v}) = df(\mathbf{v}).$$

As is clear from the diagram, the approximation $\Delta f \approx df(\mathbf{v})$ improves as $\mathbf{v}$ becomes smaller.

Lee [12] states:

> In other words, df_p [df at point p] is the linear functional that best approximates f near p ... The great power of the concept of the differential comes from the fact that we can define df invariantly on any manifold, without resorting to vague arguments involving infinitesimals.

2.2.6.2 Vectors as differential operators

At a more advanced level, the partial derivative operators $\frac{\partial}{\partial x^i}$ may be usefully regarded as basis vectors. So, for example, the standard unit basis vectors $\hat{\mathbf{e}}_x, \hat{\mathbf{e}}_y, \hat{\mathbf{e}}_z$ may be identified with the partial derivative operators $\frac{\partial}{\partial x}, \frac{\partial}{\partial y}, \frac{\partial}{\partial z}$. A vector at point P,

$$\mathbf{v} = v^1\hat{\mathbf{e}}_x + v^2\hat{\mathbf{e}}_y + v^3\hat{\mathbf{e}}_z = v^1\frac{\partial}{\partial x} + v^2\frac{\partial}{\partial y} + v^3\frac{\partial}{\partial z},$$

is then an operator waiting to act on a function f to give a number

$$\mathbf{v}f = v^1\frac{\partial f}{\partial x} + v^2\frac{\partial f}{\partial y} + v^3\frac{\partial f}{\partial z},$$

the directional derivative at P of f in the direction of $\mathbf{v}$. The differential df of a function f is then *defined* by $df(\mathbf{v}) = \mathbf{v}f$.

To see how this definition makes sense, we introduce a special type of function called a coordinate function. For example, in $\mathbb{R}^3$ we can think of x, y and z as Cartesian coordinate functions that act on a point P to pick out, respectively, the x, y and z *coordinates* of P. So for a point $P(2, 7, 1)$ we have

$$x(P) = x(2, 7, 1) = 2,$$

$$y(P) = y(2, 7, 1) = 7,$$

$$z(P) = z(2, 7, 1) = 1.$$

(We've already met an example of a coordinate function in the shape of the polar to Cartesian conversion formulas $x = r\cos\theta$ and $y = r\sin\theta$. If we feed a point $P(r, \theta)$ into $x = r\cos\theta$, out pops the x coordinate of P, and if we feed the same point into $y = r\sin\theta$, out pops the y coordinate of P.)

If we feed the coordinate function x into $df(\mathbf{v}) = \mathbf{v}f$ we get

$$dx(\mathbf{v}) = \mathbf{v}x = v^1 \frac{\partial x}{\partial x} + v^2 \frac{\partial x}{\partial y} + v^3 \frac{\partial x}{\partial z}.$$

The rate of change of the Cartesian coordinate function x in the direction of x is 1, ie $\frac{\partial x}{\partial x} = 1$. However, coordinates are independent of each other, so $\frac{\partial x}{\partial y} = \frac{\partial x}{\partial z} = 0$. Therefore

$$dx(\mathbf{v}) = \mathbf{v}x = \left(v^1 \times 1\right) + \left(v^2 \times 0\right) + \left(v^3 \times 0\right) = v^1.$$

Similarly, for the coordinate functions y and z

$$dy(\mathbf{v}) = \mathbf{v}y = v^2$$

and

$$dz(\mathbf{v}) = \mathbf{v}z = v^3.$$

And we can see that:

- the differentials dx, dy and dz of the Cartesian coordinate functions pick out, respectively, the v^1, v^2 and v^3 components of vector $\mathbf{v}$. In other words, they behave in exactly the same way as the basis 1-forms dx, dy and dz. Hence the notation dx, dy and dz (more generally, dx^i) for basis 1-forms.

Furthermore, if we set $v^1 = v^2 = v^3 = 1$ and let $\mathbf{v}$ equal, in turn, the basis vectors $\frac{\partial}{\partial x}, \frac{\partial}{\partial y}, \frac{\partial}{\partial z}$, we get

$$dx\left(\frac{\partial}{\partial x}\right) = 1, \;\; dx\left(\frac{\partial}{\partial y}\right) = 0, \;\; dx\left(\frac{\partial}{\partial z}\right) = 0,$$

$$dy\left(\frac{\partial}{\partial x}\right) = 0, \;\; dy\left(\frac{\partial}{\partial y}\right) = 1, \;\; dy\left(\frac{\partial}{\partial z}\right) = 0,$$

$$dz\left(\frac{\partial}{\partial x}\right) = 0, \;\; dz\left(\frac{\partial}{\partial y}\right) = 0, \;\; dz\left(\frac{\partial}{\partial z}\right) = 1,$$

which is equivalent to, and the justification for, (2.2.4):

$$dx(\hat{\mathbf{e}}_x) = 1, \;\; dx(\hat{\mathbf{e}}_y) = 0, \;\; dx(\hat{\mathbf{e}}_z) = 0,$$
$$dy(\hat{\mathbf{e}}_x) = 0, \;\; dy(\hat{\mathbf{e}}_y) = 1, \;\; dy(\hat{\mathbf{e}}_z) = 0,$$
$$dz(\hat{\mathbf{e}}_x) = 0, \;\; dz(\hat{\mathbf{e}}_y) = 0, \;\; dz(\hat{\mathbf{e}}_z) = 1.$$

The basis of partial derivative operators is known as the coordinate basis. Say we have general coordinates $x^1, x^2, x^3, \dots, x^n$, which are not necessarily rectangular or even orthogonal. The coordinate basis vectors for $x^1, x^2, x^3, \dots, x^n$ can be understood as follows.

There is a tangent vector that takes x^1 to 1 and all the other coordinates to 0. This tangent vector is the coordinate basis vector $\mathbf{e}_1 = \frac{\partial}{\partial x^1}$ and has components

$$\frac{\partial\left(x^1,\ldots,x^n\right)}{\partial x^1} = (1,0,\ldots,0,0)\,.$$

Similarly, the tangent vector that takes x^2 to 1 and all the other coordinates to 0 is the coordinate basis vector $\mathbf{e}_2 = \frac{\partial}{\partial x^2}$ and has components

$$\frac{\partial\left(x^1,\ldots,x^n\right)}{\partial x^2} = (0,1,\ldots,0,0)\,.$$

And the tangent vector that takes x^n to 1 and all the other coordinates to 0 is the coordinate basis vector $\mathbf{e}_n = \frac{\partial}{\partial x^n}$ and has components

$$\frac{\partial\left(x^1,\ldots,x^n\right)}{\partial x^n} = (0,0,\ldots,0,1)\,.$$

In other words, the coordinate basis vectors $\mathbf{e}_i = \frac{\partial}{\partial x^i}$ are represented by the standard basis vectors (1.2.1) of $\mathbb{R}^n$:

$$\mathbf{e}_1 = (1,0,\ldots,0,0)\,,\mathbf{e}_2 = (0,1,\ldots,0,0)\,,\ldots,\mathbf{e}_n = (0,0,\ldots,0,1)\,.$$

Finally, it's worth mentioning that writing basis vectors as $\frac{\partial}{\partial x^i}$ means we can easily derive the change of basis formula (2.2.6)

$$(\mathbf{e}_r,\mathbf{e}_\theta) = (\hat{\mathbf{e}}_x,\hat{\mathbf{e}}_y)\begin{bmatrix} \frac{\partial x}{\partial r} & \frac{\partial x}{\partial \theta} \\ \frac{\partial y}{\partial r} & \frac{\partial y}{\partial \theta} \end{bmatrix}$$

we used in section 2.2.4. Instead of writing

$$\mathbf{e}_r = \frac{\partial x}{\partial r}\hat{\mathbf{e}}_x + \frac{\partial y}{\partial r}\hat{\mathbf{e}}_y,$$

we write

$$\frac{\partial}{\partial r} = \frac{\partial x}{\partial r}\frac{\partial}{\partial x} + \frac{\partial y}{\partial r}\frac{\partial}{\partial y},$$

which is a version of the partial derivatives chain rule. Similarly, for

$$\mathbf{e}_\theta = \frac{\partial x}{\partial \theta}\hat{\mathbf{e}}_x + \frac{\partial y}{\partial \theta}\hat{\mathbf{e}}_y,$$

we write

$$\frac{\partial}{\partial \theta} = \frac{\partial x}{\partial \theta}\frac{\partial}{\partial x} + \frac{\partial y}{\partial \theta}\frac{\partial}{\partial y}.$$

Using index notation, the general change of basis formula, where $\left(x^1,\ldots,x^n\right)$ and $\left(y^1,\ldots,y^n\right)$ are, respectively, the old and new coordinate systems can be succinctly written[1] as

$$\frac{\partial}{\partial y^j} = \frac{\partial x^i}{\partial y^j}\frac{\partial}{\partial x^i},$$

---

[1] We are here using the Einstein summation convention, meaning that if a single term $\left(\frac{\partial x^i}{\partial y^j}\frac{\partial}{\partial x^i}\right)$ contains the same upper and lower index (i in this case), a sum is implied.

which is equivalent to the matrix equation

$$\left(\frac{\partial}{\partial y^1},\ldots,\frac{\partial}{\partial y^n}\right) = \left(\frac{\partial}{\partial x^1},\ldots,\frac{\partial}{\partial x^n}\right)\begin{bmatrix} \frac{\partial x^1}{\partial y^1} & \cdots & \frac{\partial x^1}{\partial y^n} \\ \vdots & & \vdots \\ \frac{\partial x^n}{\partial y^1} & \cdots & \frac{\partial x^n}{\partial y^n} \end{bmatrix},$$

where the matrix of partial derivatives

$$\frac{\partial x^i}{\partial y^j} = \begin{bmatrix} \frac{\partial x^1}{\partial y^1} & \cdots & \frac{\partial x^1}{\partial y^n} \\ \vdots & & \vdots \\ \frac{\partial x^n}{\partial y^1} & \cdots & \frac{\partial x^n}{\partial y^n} \end{bmatrix}$$

is called the Jacobian matrix.

Even though we don't use the $\frac{\partial}{\partial x^i}$ notation, we are nevertheless making implicit use of coordinate basis vectors throughout this book. Coordinates basis vectors are widely used in more advanced mathematics and physics (relativity theory, for example).

2.2.7 Another 1-form example

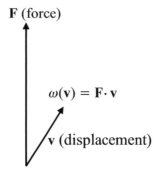

Figure 2.4: Work form ω of force field $\mathbf{F}$.

If $\mathbf{F}$ is a force field in $\mathbb{R}^3$ and $\mathbf{v}$ is a displacement vector, the work corresponding to this displacement is given by the dot product $\mathbf{F} \cdot \mathbf{v}$ (see Figure 2.4). We can also describe the work in terms of a 1-form ω acting on $\mathbf{v}$, where

$$\omega\left(\mathbf{v}\right) = \mathbf{F} \cdot \mathbf{v}.$$

41

So if we feed vector $\mathbf{v}$ to the 1-form ω, out will pop a number – the work corresponding to the displacement $\mathbf{v}$. The 1-form ω is called the work form or force 1-form of the force field $\mathbf{F}$.

In $\mathbb{R}^3$ all 1-forms are work forms of some vector field.

2.3 2-forms

2-forms and higher degree forms are multilinear alternating functions of tangent vectors. So what does that mean in plain English? Take a 3-form ω, for example, feed it three vectors $\mathbf{u}, \mathbf{v}$ and $\mathbf{w}$, and out pops a number. For the sake of argument, let's assume that number is 7, ie $\omega(\mathbf{u}, \mathbf{v}, \mathbf{w}) = 7$.

- Alternating (or antisymmetric or skew-symmetric) means if we exchange any two of the vectors, the number changes sign. For example, $\omega(\mathbf{v}, \mathbf{u}, \mathbf{w}) = -7$.

- Multilinear means that if we feed the same 3-form the vectors $2\mathbf{u}, \mathbf{v}$ and $\mathbf{w}$, the number changes to $2 \times 7 = 14$; feed ω the vectors $3\mathbf{u}, 2\mathbf{v}$ and $5\mathbf{w}$ and the number is $3 \times 2 \times 5 \times 7 = 210$.

A 2-form ω is:

- a function on a pair of vectors, which is bilinear (ie multilinear for *two* variables) and alternating, ie

$$\omega(a\mathbf{u} + b\mathbf{v}, \mathbf{w}) = a\omega(\mathbf{u}, \mathbf{w}) + b\omega(\mathbf{v}, \mathbf{w})$$

$$\omega(\mathbf{u}, \mathbf{v}) = -\omega(\mathbf{v}, \mathbf{u}),$$

  where a and b are real numbers.

On $\mathbb{R}^3$ a 2-form will include one or more of the basis 2-forms $dy \wedge dz, dz \wedge dx$ and $dx \wedge dy$ and look something like

$$\omega = f_1\, dy \wedge dz + f_2\, dz \wedge dx + f_3\, dx \wedge dy,$$

where the $\wedge$ symbol denotes a type of multiplication called the wedge product. As we'll see shortly, the wedge product is anti-commutative (ie $dx \wedge dy = -dy \wedge dx$), meaning the order of the differentials is not arbitrary.

So

$$\omega = 5\, dy \wedge dz,$$

$$\omega = 5xy\, dz \wedge dx - z\, dx \wedge dy$$

and

$$\omega = 2\, dy \wedge dz + 3y\, dz \wedge dx + dx \wedge dy$$

are all examples of 2-forms.

We can create a 2-form by multiplying (using the wedge product) two 1-forms together. For example,

$$6x\,dx \wedge 3\,dy = 18x\,dx \wedge dy.$$

In this integral

$$\int_S \underbrace{3xy\,dx \wedge dy}_{\text{2-form}},$$

$3xy\,dx \wedge dy$ is a 2-form (recall that S denotes a two-dimensional surface in $\mathbb{R}^n$).

2.3.1 The wedge product

We need a way of multiplying a p-form with a q-form to give a $(p+q)$-form. For example, we need to be able to multiply two 1-forms to give a 2-form. We do this using a type of multiplication known as the wedge product or exterior product, denoted by the symbol $\wedge$.

There's bad news and good news regarding the wedge product. The bad news is that the formula for the wedge product is tricky. Hubbard and Hubbard [11] state:

> The wedge product is a messy thing: a complicated summation, over various shuffles of vectors, of the product of two k-forms ...

However, the good news is that we don't need to worry about the formula for the wedge product. The essential takeaway for us is that the wedge product is anti-commutative for the differentials dx, dy, dz, etc. So, for example,

$$dx \wedge dy = -dy \wedge dx.$$

Which means, in turn, that the wedge product is anti-commutative for the general 1-forms ω and ν, ie

$$\omega \wedge \nu = -\nu \wedge \omega.$$

Algebra that makes use of the wedge product is known as exterior algebra. Thankfully, the only difference between exterior and ordinary algebra is the anti-commutativity rule.

The intuitive motivation for the wedge product is that it allows n vector-like objects (vectors or differential forms, for example) to be combined in a geometrical fashion to give an n-dimensional area or volume. The wedge product of two vectors $\mathbf{u}$ and $\mathbf{v}$ can be represented by a parallelogram spanned by $\mathbf{u}$ and $\mathbf{v}$ as shown in Figure 2.5

Notice that the order of the two vectors matters: $\mathbf{u} \wedge \mathbf{v}$ has a clockwise orientation, $\mathbf{v} \wedge \mathbf{u}$ has a counterclockwise orientation. The notion of orientation, which we'll discuss in chapter 6, is the rationale for the wedge product anti-commutativity rule.

We can informally derive that rule by considering dx as an infinitesimal displacement along the x axis. The parallelogram spanned by two such dx will have zero area (a

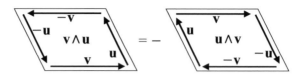

Figure 2.5: The wedge product and orientation.

parallelogram with sides spanned by the same vector is a straight line). We can write this as

$$dx \wedge dx = 0.$$

It must follow that

$$(dx + dy) \wedge (dx + dy) = 0,$$

which we can expand to get

$$(dx \wedge dx) + (dx \wedge dy) + (dy \wedge dx) + (dy \wedge dy) = 0.$$

Because

$$(dx \wedge dy) + (dy \wedge dx) = 0,$$

we have

$$dx \wedge dy = -dy \wedge dx,$$

and we have shown that the wedge product is anti-commutative.

Using index notation, we can generalise $dx \wedge dx = 0$ to

$$dx^i \wedge dx^i = 0, \tag{2.3.1}$$

and conclude that the wedge product of any 1-form with itself is zero.

Functions commute with dx, ie

$$f \wedge dx = dx \wedge f.$$

The convention is not to use the $\wedge$ when multiplying a form by a function, ie to write $f\,dx$ and not $f \wedge dx$.

Example 2.1. Calculate the wedge product $\omega \wedge \nu$ and $\nu \wedge \omega$ of the 1-forms $\omega = 3\,dx - 5\,dy$ and $\nu = dx + 2\,dy$.

$$\omega \wedge \nu = (3\,dx - 5\,dy)\,(dx + 2\,dy)$$

$$= 3\,dx \wedge dx + 6\,dx \wedge dy - 5\,dy \wedge dx - 10\,dy \wedge dy$$

$$= 11\,dx \wedge dy,$$

because $dx \wedge dx = dy \wedge dy = 0$ and $-5\,dy \wedge dx = 5\,dx \wedge dy$.

$$\nu \wedge \omega = (dx + 2\,dy)\,(3\,dx - 5\,dy)$$

$$= 3\,dx \wedge dx - 5\,dx \wedge dy + 6\,dy \wedge dx - 10\,dy \wedge dy$$

$$= -11\,dx \wedge dy,$$

because $dx \wedge dx = dy \wedge dy = 0$ and $6\,dy \wedge dx = -6\,dx \wedge dy$. And we can see that $\omega \wedge \nu = -\nu \wedge \omega$.

Example 2.2. Calculate the wedge product of the 1-forms $\omega = u_1 dx + u_2 dy + u_3 dz$ and $\nu = v_1 dx + v_2 dy + v_3 dz$.

$$\omega \wedge \nu = (u_1 dx + u_2 dy + u_3 dz) \wedge (v_1 dx + v_2 dy + v_3 dz)$$

$$= u_1 dx \wedge v_1 dx + u_1 dx \wedge v_2 dy + u_1 dx \wedge v_3 dz$$
$$+ u_2 dy \wedge v_1 dx + u_2 dy \wedge v_2 dy + u_2 dy \wedge v_3 dz$$
$$+ u_3 dz \wedge v_1 dx + u_3 dz \wedge v_2 dy + u_3 dz \wedge v_3 dz.$$

Which simplifies to give the 2-form

$$\omega \wedge \nu = (u_2 v_3 - u_3 v_2)\,dy \wedge dz + (u_3 v_1 - u_1 v_3)\,dz \wedge dx + (u_1 v_2 - u_2 v_1)\,dx \wedge dy,$$

because $u_1 dx \wedge v_1 dx = u_2 dy \wedge v_2 dy = u_3 dz \wedge v_3 dz = 0$ and $dy \wedge dz = -dz \wedge dy$, $dz \wedge dx = -dx \wedge dz$ and $dx \wedge dy = -dy \wedge dx$.

Notice that if we let $u_1 = u^1$, $u_2 = u^2$, $u_3 = u^3$, $v_1 = v^1$, $v_2 = v^2$ and $v_3 = v^3$, then the coefficients of this 2-form $\omega \wedge \nu$ are the same as the components of the cross product (1.6.1) of the vectors $\mathbf{u} = u^1 \hat{\mathbf{e}}_x + u^2 \hat{\mathbf{e}}_y + u^3 \hat{\mathbf{e}}_z$ and $\mathbf{v} = v^1 \hat{\mathbf{e}}_x + v^2 \hat{\mathbf{e}}_y + v^3 \hat{\mathbf{e}}_z$:

$$\mathbf{u} \times \mathbf{v} = \left(u^2 v^3 - u^3 v^2\right) \hat{\mathbf{e}}_x + \left(u^3 v^1 - u^1 v^3\right) \hat{\mathbf{e}}_y + \left(u^1 v^2 - u^2 v^1\right) \hat{\mathbf{e}}_z.$$

We can therefore regard the wedge product as an n-dimensional generalisation of the three-dimensional cross product.

Moving on, we can now see why there are no 4-forms or higher in $\mathbb{R}^3$. If we multiply together any four of the differentials dx, dy, dz, we must have at least two of the same and the result will be zero. For example,

$$dx \wedge dy \wedge dz \wedge dx$$

$$= -dx \wedge dy \wedge dx \wedge dz$$

$$= dx \wedge dx \wedge dy \wedge dz = 0,$$

because $dx \wedge dx = 0$.

Therefore, an n-dimensional space M can have up to n-dimensional differential forms.

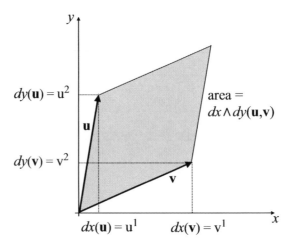

Figure 2.6: $dx \wedge dy$ acting on vectors **u** and **v** in $\mathbb{R}^2$.

2.3.2 2-forms acting on two vectors

We've seen how a 1-form acts on a vector to give a number. A 2-form acts on a pair of vectors to give a number, ie a 2-form is a function that requires two vector arguments. Let's see how this works in $\mathbb{R}^2$ with a couple of vectors $\mathbf{u} = \left(u^1, u^2\right)$ and $\mathbf{v} = \left(v^1, v^2\right)$, as shown in Figure 2.6. A natural number defined from **u** and **v** is the (signed) area of the parallelogram they span. We know from when we looked at determinants in section 1.7 that the signed area of the parallelogram spanned by **u** and **v** is given by

$$\begin{vmatrix} u^1 & v^1 \\ u^2 & v^2 \end{vmatrix} = u^1 v^2 - u^2 v^1.$$

Because dx^i picks out a vector's ith component, we can also write this as

$$dx \wedge dy\left(\mathbf{u}, \mathbf{v}\right) = \begin{vmatrix} dx\left(\mathbf{u}\right) & dx\left(\mathbf{v}\right) \\ dy\left(\mathbf{u}\right) & dy\left(\mathbf{v}\right) \end{vmatrix} = \begin{vmatrix} u^1 & v^1 \\ u^2 & v^2 \end{vmatrix} = u^1 v^2 - u^2 v^1,$$

where we *define* the signed area of the parallelogram spanned by **u** and **v** to be the value of $dx \wedge dy\left(\mathbf{u}, \mathbf{v}\right).$

Earlier, in section 2.2.3, when looking at 1-forms, we saw that $dx^i\left(\mathbf{v}\right)$ gives the projection of vector **v** onto the x^ith coordinate axis. We can also make use of the geometric notion of projection in order to understand how higher degree forms act on vectors. We've just seen that for two vectors **u** and **v** in $\mathbb{R}^2$, $dx \wedge dy\left(\mathbf{u}, \mathbf{v}\right)$ gives the signed area of the parallelogram spanned by $\mathbf{u}$ and $\mathbf{v}$ in $\mathbb{R}^2$ itself. Therefore, $dx \wedge dy$ projects onto the *whole* space of $\mathbb{R}^2$.

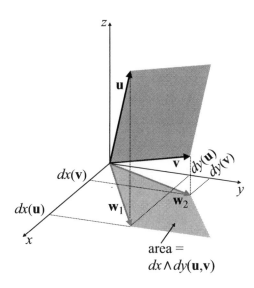

$$\text{area} = dx \wedge dy(\mathbf{u,v})$$

Figure 2.7: $dx \wedge dy$ acting on vectors $\mathbf{u}$ and $\mathbf{v}$ in $\mathbb{R}^3$.

Now let's see how this works in $\mathbb{R}^3$ with vectors $\mathbf{u} = \left(u^1, u^2, u^3\right)$ and $\mathbf{v} = \left(v^1, v^2, v^3\right)$, as shown in Figure 2.7.

Again using the basis 1-forms dx and dy, we can define two new vectors on the xy plane: $\mathbf{w}_1$ with components $dx(\mathbf{u}) = u^1$ and $dy(\mathbf{u}) = u^2$, and $\mathbf{w}_2$ with components $dx(\mathbf{v}) = v^1$ and $dy(\mathbf{v}) = v^2$. The value of $dx \wedge dy(\mathbf{u}, \mathbf{v})$ then equals the signed area of the parallelogram spanned by $\mathbf{w}_1$ and $\mathbf{w}_2$.

In other words, the parallelogram spanned by $\mathbf{w}_1$ and $\mathbf{w}_2$ is the projection onto the xy plane of the parallelogram spanned by $\mathbf{u}$ and $\mathbf{v}$. The 2-form $dx \wedge dy$ allows us to find the area of that projected parallelogram, which is given by $dx \wedge dy(\mathbf{u}, \mathbf{v})$. The area of the projected parallelogram in the xz plane would be given by $dx \wedge dz(\mathbf{u}, \mathbf{v})$. And the area of the projected parallelogram in the yz plane would be given by $dy \wedge dz(\mathbf{u}, \mathbf{v})$.

It's easy to see that if we used $a\,dx \wedge dy$ (where a is a constant) instead of $dx \wedge dy$, the value of $a\,dx \wedge dz(\mathbf{u}, \mathbf{v})$ would be given by

$$a\,dx \wedge dy(\mathbf{u}, \mathbf{v}) = a \begin{vmatrix} dx(\mathbf{u}) & dx(\mathbf{v}) \\ dy(\mathbf{u}) & dy(\mathbf{v}) \end{vmatrix} = a \begin{vmatrix} u^1 & v^1 \\ u^2 & v^2 \end{vmatrix} = a\left(u^1 v^2 - u^2 v^1\right), \quad (2.3.2)$$

which can be interpreted as the area of the projected parallelogram in the xy plane multiplied by the factor a.

Similarly, if we had a 2-form $\omega = a\,dy \wedge dz + b\,dz \wedge dx + c\,dx \wedge dy$, the value of ω acting on $\mathbf{u}$ and $\mathbf{v}$ can be visualised as the area of the projected parallelogram in the yz plane multiplied by the factor a, plus the area of the projected parallelogram in the zx plane multiplied by the factor b, plus the area of the projected parallelogram in the xy plane multiplied by the factor c.

Example 2.3. From Bryan [7]. Find the value of the 2-form
$\omega = (x+2z)\,dx \wedge dy + y\,dx \wedge dz$ acting on the vectors $\mathbf{v}_1 = (1,3,3)$ and $\mathbf{v}_2 = (-1,0,7)$ at the point $(1,1,5)$.

So we need to evaluate $\omega(\mathbf{v}_1, \mathbf{v}_2)$ at the point $(1,1,5)$. Utilising (2.3.2), we can write

$$\omega(\mathbf{v}_1, \mathbf{v}_2) = ((x+2z)\,dx \wedge dy + y\,dx \wedge dz)(\mathbf{v}_1, \mathbf{v}_2)$$

$$= (x+2z) \begin{vmatrix} dx(\mathbf{v}_1) & dx(\mathbf{v}_2) \\ dy(\mathbf{v}_1) & dy(\mathbf{v}_2) \end{vmatrix} + y \begin{vmatrix} dx(\mathbf{v}_1) & dx(\mathbf{v}_2) \\ dz(\mathbf{v}_1) & dz(\mathbf{v}_2) \end{vmatrix}$$

$$= (x+2z) \begin{vmatrix} dx(1,3,3) & dx(-1,0,7) \\ dy(1,3,3) & dy(-1,0,7) \end{vmatrix} + y \begin{vmatrix} dx(1,3,3) & dx(-1,0,7) \\ dz(1,3,3) & dz(-1,0,7) \end{vmatrix}$$

$$= (x+2z) \begin{vmatrix} 1 & -1 \\ 3 & 0 \end{vmatrix} + y \begin{vmatrix} 1 & -1 \\ 3 & 7 \end{vmatrix}$$

$$= 3(x+2z) + 10y$$

$$= 3x + 10y + 6z.$$

At the point $(1,1,5)$ this equals 43.

Remember the determinant!   We saw in section 1.7 that determinants are alternating multilinear functions of their columns (or rows). Because we naturally use determinants to calculate wedge products, those two properties also transfer over to differential forms. Feel free to convince yourself of this using the previous example:

- Alternating – If we reverse the order of the two vectors and evaluate $\omega(\mathbf{v}_2, \mathbf{v}_1)$ instead of $\omega(\mathbf{v}_1, \mathbf{v}_2)$, we end up with -43 instead of 43.

- Multilinearity – If we multiply one of the vectors, $\mathbf{v}_2$ for example, by a constant k and evaluate $\omega(\mathbf{v}_1, k\mathbf{v}_2)$ instead of $\omega(\mathbf{v}_1, \mathbf{v}_2)$, we end up with $43k$ instead of 43.

In general, the wedge product of two 1-forms ω_1 and ω_2 acting on two vectors $\mathbf{v}_1$ and $\mathbf{v}_2$ is given by

$$(\omega_1 \wedge \omega_2)(\mathbf{v}_1, \mathbf{v}_2) = \begin{vmatrix} \omega_1(\mathbf{v}_1) & \omega_1(\mathbf{v}_2) \\ \omega_2(\mathbf{v}_1) & \omega_2(\mathbf{v}_2) \end{vmatrix}. \tag{2.3.3}$$

2.3.3 2-form example

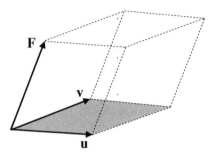

Figure 2.8: Flux through a surface is a 2-form.

Working in $\mathbb{R}^3$, Figure 2.8 shows a surface, the shaded parallelogram, spanned by $\mathbf{u}$ and $\mathbf{v}$. If $\mathbf{F}$ represents constant fluid flow through that surface, then the flux (flow per unit time) of the fluid through the shaded area is equal to the volume of the parallelepiped spanned by $\mathbf{u}, \mathbf{v}$ and $\mathbf{F}$, ie by the determinant

$$|\mathbf{F}, \mathbf{u}, \mathbf{v}| = \begin{vmatrix} F_1 & u^1 & v^1 \\ F_2 & u^2 & v^2 \\ F_3 & u^3 & v^3 \end{vmatrix},$$

which also happens to be the scalar triple product

$$\mathbf{F} \cdot (\mathbf{u} \times \mathbf{v}) = |\mathbf{F}, \mathbf{u}, \mathbf{v}| = \begin{vmatrix} F_1 & u^1 & v^1 \\ F_2 & u^2 & v^2 \\ F_3 & u^3 & v^3 \end{vmatrix}.$$

We can also describe the flux in terms of a 2-form ω acting on $\mathbf{u}$ and $\mathbf{v}$, where

$$\omega\left(\mathbf{u}, \mathbf{v}\right) = \mathbf{F} \cdot \left(\mathbf{u} \times \mathbf{v}\right) = |\mathbf{F}, \mathbf{u}, \mathbf{v}| = \begin{vmatrix} F_1 & u^1 & v^1 \\ F_2 & u^2 & v^2 \\ F_3 & u^3 & v^3 \end{vmatrix}. \qquad (2.3.4)$$

The 2-form ω is called the flux form of $\mathbf{F}$.

In $\mathbb{R}^3$ all 2-forms are flux forms of some vector field.

2.3.4 Surfaces

A surface is a two-dimensional manifold and can be parameterised by two parameters, u and v for example. So in $\mathbb{R}^3$ we might have a surface (in this case a cone open along the x axis) described by the parametric equation

$$\mathbf{\Phi}\left(u,v\right) = \left(u, u\cos v, u\sin v\right),$$

which means

$$x = u, \; y = u\cos v, \; z = u\sin v.$$

Tangent vectors to this surface are given by

$$\frac{\partial\mathbf{\Phi}}{\partial u} = \left(\frac{\partial x}{\partial u}, \frac{\partial y}{\partial u}, \frac{\partial z}{\partial u}\right) = \left(1, \cos v, \sin v\right)$$

and

$$\frac{\partial\mathbf{\Phi}}{\partial v} = \left(\frac{\partial x}{\partial v}, \frac{\partial y}{\partial v}, \frac{\partial z}{\partial v}\right) = \left(0, -u\sin v, u\cos v\right).$$

We can show a 2-form ω acting on the tangent vectors $\frac{\partial\mathbf{\Phi}}{\partial u}$ and $\frac{\partial\mathbf{\Phi}}{\partial v}$ by

$$\omega\left(\frac{\partial\mathbf{\Phi}}{\partial u}, \frac{\partial\mathbf{\Phi}}{\partial v}\right).$$

Earlier, when we were looking at how a 2-form acts on two vectors, we noted that (2.3.3)

$$\left(\omega_1 \wedge \omega_2\right)\left(\mathbf{v}_1, \mathbf{v}_2\right) = \begin{vmatrix} \omega_1\left(\mathbf{v}_1\right) & \omega_1\left(\mathbf{v}_2\right) \\ \omega_2\left(\mathbf{v}_1\right) & \omega_2\left(\mathbf{v}_2\right) \end{vmatrix},$$

which works equally well if we write $\mathbf{v}_1$ and $\mathbf{v}_2$ explicitly as tangent vectors. For example, if we let $\omega_1 = dx$ and $\omega_2 = dy$, and substitute $\frac{\partial\mathbf{\Phi}}{\partial u}$ for $\mathbf{v}_1$ and $\frac{\partial\mathbf{\Phi}}{\partial v}$ for $\mathbf{v}_2$, we obtain

$$\left(dx \wedge dy\right)\left(\frac{\partial\mathbf{\Phi}}{\partial u}, \frac{\partial\mathbf{\Phi}}{\partial v}\right) = \begin{vmatrix} dx\left(\frac{\partial\mathbf{\Phi}}{\partial u}\right) & dx\left(\frac{\partial\mathbf{\Phi}}{\partial v}\right) \\ dy\left(\frac{\partial\mathbf{\Phi}}{\partial u}\right) & dy\left(\frac{\partial\mathbf{\Phi}}{\partial v}\right) \end{vmatrix}$$

$$\left(dx \wedge dy\right)\left(\frac{\partial\mathbf{\Phi}}{\partial u}, \frac{\partial\mathbf{\Phi}}{\partial v}\right) = \begin{vmatrix} \frac{\partial x}{\partial u} & \frac{\partial x}{\partial v} \\ \frac{\partial y}{\partial u} & \frac{\partial y}{\partial v} \end{vmatrix}. \tag{2.3.5}$$

Similarly, we find

$$\left(dy \wedge dz\right)\left(\frac{\partial\mathbf{\Phi}}{\partial u}, \frac{\partial\mathbf{\Phi}}{\partial v}\right) = \begin{vmatrix} \frac{\partial y}{\partial u} & \frac{\partial y}{\partial v} \\ \frac{\partial z}{\partial u} & \frac{\partial z}{\partial v} \end{vmatrix}$$

and

$$\left(dz \wedge dx\right)\left(\frac{\partial\mathbf{\Phi}}{\partial u}, \frac{\partial\mathbf{\Phi}}{\partial v}\right) = \begin{vmatrix} \frac{\partial z}{\partial u} & \frac{\partial z}{\partial v} \\ \frac{\partial x}{\partial u} & \frac{\partial x}{\partial v} \end{vmatrix}.$$

2.4 3-forms and higher

We've just seen that a 2-form is a multilinear alternating function of two tangent vectors. Likewise, a 3-form is an alternating multilinear function of three tangent vectors, and a k-form (where $k > 3$) is an alternating multilinear function of k tangent vectors.

On $\mathbb{R}^3$ a 3-form will be a function of the basis 3-form $dx \wedge dy \wedge dz$:

$$\omega = f(x, y, z)\, dx \wedge dy \wedge dz,$$

and can be constructed, using the wedge product, out of lower-order forms.

In this integral:

$$\int_M \underbrace{5z\, dx \wedge dy \wedge dz}_{\text{3-form}},$$

where M denotes a region of $\mathbb{R}^3$, $5z\, dx \wedge dy \wedge dz$ is a 3-form.

Again, because the wedge product is anti-commutative, the order of the differentials dx, dy and dz is not arbitrary.

2.4.1 3-forms acting on three vectors

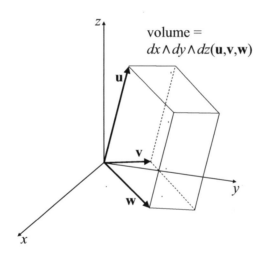

Figure 2.9: $dx \wedge dy \wedge dz$ acting on vectors $\mathbf{u}, \mathbf{v}$ and $\mathbf{w}$ in $\mathbb{R}^3$.

A 3-form acts on three vectors to give a number, ie a 3-form is a function that requires three vector arguments. Let's see how this works in $\mathbb{R}^3$ with the vectors $\mathbf{u} = \left(u^1, u^2, u^3\right)$, $\mathbf{v} = \left(v^1, v^2, v^3\right)$ and $\mathbf{w} = \left(w^1, w^2, w^3\right)$, as shown in Figure 2.9. Earlier, when looking at the 2-form $dx \wedge dy$, we said that a natural number defined from the two vectors $\mathbf{u}$ and $\mathbf{v}$ is the (signed) area of the parallelogram they span. which we then defined to be the value of $dx \wedge dy\,(\mathbf{u}, \mathbf{v})$. In a similar fashion, we can define the value of the basis

3-form $dx \wedge dy \wedge dz$ acting on the three vectors $\mathbf{u}, \mathbf{v}$ and $\mathbf{w}$ as the signed volume of the parallelepiped they span. This signed volume is given by the determinant

$$\begin{vmatrix} u^1 & v^1 & w^1 \\ u^2 & v^2 & w^2 \\ u^3 & v^3 & w^3 \end{vmatrix}.$$

Again we recall that dx^i picks out a vector's ith component and justify our definition by writing

$$dx \wedge dy \wedge dz\,(\mathbf{u}, \mathbf{v}, \mathbf{w}) = \begin{vmatrix} dx\,(\mathbf{u}) & dx\,(\mathbf{v}) & dx\,(\mathbf{w}) \\ dy\,(\mathbf{u}) & dy\,(\mathbf{v}) & dy\,(\mathbf{w}) \\ dz\,(\mathbf{u}) & dz\,(\mathbf{v}) & dz\,(\mathbf{w}) \end{vmatrix} = \begin{vmatrix} u^1 & v^1 & w^1 \\ u^2 & v^2 & w^2 \\ u^3 & v^3 & w^3 \end{vmatrix}.$$

Just as we did with the 2-form $dx \wedge dy$, we can now ask what space does the 3-form $dx \wedge dy \wedge dz$ project $\mathbf{u}, \mathbf{v}$ and $\mathbf{w}$ onto in $\mathbb{R}^3$? We've just seen that $dx \wedge dy \wedge dz\,(\mathbf{u}, \mathbf{v}, \mathbf{w})$ gives the signed volume of the parallelepiped spanned by $\mathbf{u}, \mathbf{v}$ and $\mathbf{w}$ in $\mathbb{R}^3$. Therefore, $dx \wedge dy \wedge dz$ projects onto the *whole* space of $\mathbb{R}^3$.

Now let's exercise our mathematical imaginations and explore what happens if we have a 3-form $dx^1 \wedge dx^2 \wedge dx^3$ acting on three vectors $\mathbf{v}_1 = (1, 2, -1, 1)$, $\mathbf{v}_2 = (3, -2, 1, 2)$ and $\mathbf{v}_3 = (0, 1, 2, 1)$ in $\mathbb{R}^4$, using x^1, x^2, x^3, x^4 coordinates. The vectors $\mathbf{v}_1, \mathbf{v}_2$ and $\mathbf{v}_3$ span a parallelepiped in $\mathbb{R}^4$. Using $dx^1 \wedge dx^2 \wedge dx^3$ we define three new vectors $\mathbf{w}_1, \mathbf{w}_2$ and $\mathbf{w}_3$:

$$\mathbf{w}_1 = dx^1 \wedge dx^2 \wedge dx^3\,(\mathbf{v}_1) = (1, 2, -1)\,,$$

$$\mathbf{w}_2 = dx^1 \wedge dx^2 \wedge dx^3\,(\mathbf{v}_2) = (3, -2, 1)\,,$$

$$\mathbf{w}_3 = dx^1 \wedge dx^2 \wedge dx^3\,(\mathbf{v}_3) = (0, 1, 2)\,.$$

The parallelepiped spanned by $\mathbf{w}_1, \mathbf{w}_2$ and $\mathbf{w}_3$ is the projection onto the $x_1 x_2 x_3$ subspace of $\mathbb{R}^4$ of the parallelepiped spanned by $\mathbf{v}_1, \mathbf{v}_2$ and $\mathbf{v}_3$. The value of $dx^1 \wedge dx^2 \wedge dx^3\,(\mathbf{v}_1, \mathbf{v}_2, \mathbf{v}_3)$ then gives the volume of that projected parallelepiped, ie

$$dx^1 \wedge dx^2 \wedge dx^3\,(\mathbf{v}_1, \mathbf{v}_2, \mathbf{v}_3) = \begin{vmatrix} dx^1\,(\mathbf{v}_1) & dx^1\,(\mathbf{v}_2) & dx^1\,(\mathbf{v}_3) \\ dx^2\,(\mathbf{v}_1) & dx^2\,(\mathbf{v}_2) & dx^2\,(\mathbf{v}_3) \\ dx^3\,(\mathbf{v}_1) & dx^3\,(\mathbf{v}_2) & dx^3\,(\mathbf{v}_3) \end{vmatrix}.$$

If we used $a\, dx^1 \wedge dx^2 \wedge dx^3$ (where a is a constant) instead of $dx^1 \wedge dx^2 \wedge dx^3$, the value of $a\, dx^1 \wedge dx^2 \wedge dx^3\,(\mathbf{v}_1, \mathbf{v}_2, \mathbf{v}_3)$ can be interpreted as the volume of the projected parallelepiped in the $x_1 x_2 x_3$ subspace of $\mathbb{R}^4$ multiplied by the factor a.

Similarly, if we had a general 3-form in $\mathbb{R}^4$

$$\omega = a\, dx^1 \wedge dx^2 \wedge dx^3 + b\, dx^1 \wedge dx^2 \wedge dx^4 + c\, dx^1 \wedge dx^3 \wedge dx^4 + d\, dx^2 \wedge dx^3 \wedge dx^4,$$

(where a, b, c and d are constants), the value of ω acting on $\mathbf{v}_1, \mathbf{v}_2$ and $\mathbf{v}_3$ can be visualised as the area of the projected parallelogram in the $x_1 x_2 x_3$ subspace multiplied by the factor a, plus the area of the projected parallelogram in the $x_1 x_2 x_4$ subspace multiplied by the factor b, plus the area of the projected parallelogram in the $x_1 x_3 x_4$ subspace multiplied by the factor c, plus the area of the projected parallelogram in the $x_2 x_3 x_4$ subspace multiplied by the factor d.

In general, the wedge product of three 1-forms ω_1, ω_2 and ω_3 acting on three vectors $\mathbf{v}_1, \mathbf{v}_2$ and $\mathbf{v}_3$ is given by

$$\omega_1 \wedge \omega_2 \wedge \omega_3 (\mathbf{v}_1, \mathbf{v}_2, \mathbf{v}_3) = \begin{vmatrix} \omega_1(\mathbf{v}_1) & \omega_1(\mathbf{v}_2) & \omega_1(\mathbf{v}_3) \\ \omega_2(\mathbf{v}_1) & \omega_2(\mathbf{v}_2) & \omega_2(\mathbf{v}_3) \\ \omega_3(\mathbf{v}_1) & \omega_3(\mathbf{v}_2) & \omega_3(\mathbf{v}_3) \end{vmatrix}. \qquad (2.4.1)$$

To generalise (2.4.1), the wedge product of k 1-forms $\omega_1, \cdots, \omega_k$ acting on k vectors $\mathbf{v}_1, \ldots, \mathbf{v}_k$ is given by

$$(\omega_1 \wedge \cdots \wedge \omega_k)(\mathbf{v}_1, \ldots, \mathbf{v}_k) = \begin{vmatrix} \omega_1(\mathbf{v}_1) & \cdots & \omega_1(\mathbf{v}_k) \\ \vdots & & \vdots \\ \omega_k(\mathbf{v}_1) & \cdots & \omega_k(\mathbf{v}_k) \end{vmatrix}.$$

Example 2.4. From Hubbard and Hubbard [11]. Find the value of the basis 3-form $dx^1 \wedge dx^2 \wedge dx^4$ acting on the vectors $\mathbf{v}_1 = (1, 2, -1, 1)$, $\mathbf{v}_2 = (3, -2, 1, 2)$ and $\mathbf{v}_3 = (0, 1, 2, 1)$.

Equation (2.4.1)

$$(\omega_1 \wedge \omega_2 \wedge \omega_3)(\mathbf{v}_1, \mathbf{v}_2, \mathbf{v}_3) = \begin{vmatrix} \omega_1(\mathbf{v}_1) & \omega_1(\mathbf{v}_2) & \omega_1(\mathbf{v}_3) \\ \omega_2(\mathbf{v}_1) & \omega_2(\mathbf{v}_2) & \omega_2(\mathbf{v}_3) \\ \omega_3(\mathbf{v}_1) & \omega_3(\mathbf{v}_2) & \omega_3(\mathbf{v}_3) \end{vmatrix},$$

becomes, for our example,

$$\left(dx^1 \wedge dx^2 \wedge dx^4\right)(\mathbf{v}_1, \mathbf{v}_2, \mathbf{v}_3) = \begin{vmatrix} dx^1(\mathbf{v}_1) & dx^1(\mathbf{v}_2) & dx^1(\mathbf{v}_3) \\ dx^2(\mathbf{v}_1) & dx^2(\mathbf{v}_2) & dx^2(\mathbf{v}_3) \\ dx^4(\mathbf{v}_1) & dx^4(\mathbf{v}_2) & dx^4(\mathbf{v}_3) \end{vmatrix}$$

$$= \begin{vmatrix} 1 & 3 & 0 \\ 2 & -2 & 1 \\ 1 & 2 & 1 \end{vmatrix}$$

$$= -7.$$

You might like to confirm the alternating and multilinear properties of the 3-form $dx^1 \wedge dx^2 \wedge dx^4$ in the previous example:

- Alternating – If we exchange any two of the vectors in $\left(dx^1 \wedge dx^2 \wedge dx^4\right)(\mathbf{v}_1, \mathbf{v}_2, \mathbf{v}_3)$, we end up with 7 instead of -7.

- Multilinear – If we multiply one of the vectors, $\mathbf{v}_2$ for example, by a constant k and evaluate $\left(dx^1 \wedge dx^2 \wedge dx^4\right)(\mathbf{v}_1, k\mathbf{v}_2, \mathbf{v}_3)$ instead of $\left(dx^1 \wedge dx^2 \wedge dx^4\right)(\mathbf{v}_1, \mathbf{v}_2, \mathbf{v}_3)$, we end up with $-7k$ instead of -7.

2.4.2 3-form example

Referring again to Figure 2.8, the oriented volume of the parallelepiped spanned by $\mathbf{u}, \mathbf{v}$ and $\mathbf{F}$ is a 3-form ω, where

$$\omega\left(\mathbf{F}, \mathbf{u}, \mathbf{v}\right) = \begin{vmatrix} F_1 & u^1 & v^1 \\ F_2 & u^2 & v^2 \\ F_3 & u^3 & v^3 \end{vmatrix}.$$

In $\mathbb{R}^3$ 3-forms are sometimes called density forms. If the function $f\left(x, y, z\right)$ in the general 3-form

$$\omega = f\left(x, y, z\right) dx \wedge dy \wedge dz$$

describes something (mass, for example) per unit volume – ie is a density function – we can integrate ω to find the total amount of that something.

2.4.3 Three and higher dimensional spaces

A three-dimensional manifold can be parameterised by three parameters, u, v and w for example, and described by a parametric equation $\mathbf{\Phi}\left(u, v, w\right)$. If we have a three-dimensional manifold in $\mathbb{R}^4$ (with coordinates x^1, x^2, x^3, x^4), the tangent vectors are

$$\frac{\partial \mathbf{\Phi}}{\partial u} = \left(\frac{\partial x^1}{\partial u}, \frac{\partial x^2}{\partial u}, \frac{\partial x^3}{\partial u}, \frac{\partial x^4}{\partial u}\right),$$

$$\frac{\partial \mathbf{\Phi}}{\partial v} = \left(\frac{\partial x^1}{\partial v}, \frac{\partial x^2}{\partial v}, \frac{\partial x^3}{\partial v}, \frac{\partial x^4}{\partial v}\right)$$

and

$$\frac{\partial \mathbf{\Phi}}{\partial w} = \left(\frac{\partial x^1}{\partial w}, \frac{\partial x^2}{\partial w}, \frac{\partial x^3}{\partial w}, \frac{\partial x^4}{\partial w}\right).$$

We can show a 3-form ω acting on the tangent vectors $\frac{\partial \mathbf{\Phi}}{\partial u}$, $\frac{\partial \mathbf{\Phi}}{\partial v}$ and $\frac{\partial \mathbf{\Phi}}{\partial w}$ by

$$\omega\left(\frac{\partial \mathbf{\Phi}}{\partial u}, \frac{\partial \mathbf{\Phi}}{\partial v}, \frac{\partial \mathbf{\Phi}}{\partial w}\right).$$

Equation (2.4.1)

$$\left(\omega_1 \wedge \omega_2 \wedge \omega_3\right)\left(\mathbf{v}_1, \mathbf{v}_2, \mathbf{v}_3\right) = \begin{vmatrix} \omega_1\left(\mathbf{v}_1\right) & \omega_1\left(\mathbf{v}_2\right) & \omega_1\left(\mathbf{v}_3\right) \\ \omega_2\left(\mathbf{v}_1\right) & \omega_2\left(\mathbf{v}_2\right) & \omega_2\left(\mathbf{v}_3\right) \\ \omega_3\left(\mathbf{v}_1\right) & \omega_3\left(\mathbf{v}_2\right) & \omega_3\left(\mathbf{v}_3\right) \end{vmatrix}$$

tells us how a 3-form acts on three vectors. If, for example, our 3-form $\omega = dx^1 \wedge dx^2 \wedge dx^4$, we can rewrite this equation in terms of tangent vectors as

$$\left(dx^1 \wedge dx^2 \wedge dx^4\right)\left(\frac{\partial \mathbf{\Phi}}{\partial u}, \frac{\partial \mathbf{\Phi}}{\partial v}, \frac{\partial \mathbf{\Phi}}{\partial w}\right) = \begin{vmatrix} dx^1\left(\frac{\partial \mathbf{\Phi}}{\partial u}\right) & dx^1\left(\frac{\partial \mathbf{\Phi}}{\partial v}\right) & dx^1\left(\frac{\partial \mathbf{\Phi}}{\partial w}\right) \\ dx^2\left(\frac{\partial \mathbf{\Phi}}{\partial u}\right) & dx^2\left(\frac{\partial \mathbf{\Phi}}{\partial v}\right) & dx^2\left(\frac{\partial \mathbf{\Phi}}{\partial w}\right) \\ dx^4\left(\frac{\partial \mathbf{\Phi}}{\partial u}\right) & dx^4\left(\frac{\partial \mathbf{\Phi}}{\partial v}\right) & dx^4\left(\frac{\partial \mathbf{\Phi}}{\partial w}\right) \end{vmatrix}$$

$$= \begin{vmatrix} \frac{\partial x^1}{\partial u} & \frac{\partial x^1}{\partial v} & \frac{\partial x^1}{\partial w} \\ \frac{\partial x^2}{\partial u} & \frac{\partial x^2}{\partial v} & \frac{\partial x^2}{\partial w} \\ \frac{\partial x^4}{\partial u} & \frac{\partial x^4}{\partial v} & \frac{\partial x^4}{\partial w} \end{vmatrix}. \tag{2.4.2}$$

Hopefully, you can now see the pattern for differential forms of higher dimension. For example, a k-form $\omega = dx^1 \wedge \cdots \wedge dx^k$ acting on k tangent vectors $\left(\frac{\partial \mathbf{\Phi}}{\partial u^1}, \ldots, \frac{\partial \mathbf{\Phi}}{\partial u^k}\right)$ in $\mathbb{R}^k$ would be given by

$$\left(dx^1 \wedge \cdots \wedge dx^k\right) \left(\frac{\partial \mathbf{\Phi}}{\partial u^1}, \ldots, \frac{\partial \mathbf{\Phi}}{\partial u^k}\right) = \begin{vmatrix} \frac{\partial x^1}{\partial u^1} & \cdots & \frac{\partial x^1}{\partial u^k} \\ \vdots & & \vdots \\ \frac{\partial x^k}{\partial u^1} & \cdots & \frac{\partial x^k}{\partial u^k} \end{vmatrix}.$$

And so on.

3 Converting between differential forms and vectors

In $\mathbb{R}^3$ differential forms nicely correspond with various scalar and vector fields. We'll be using these correspondences in subsequent chapters to derive some useful vector calculus formulas.

3.1 0-forms

We've already noted that a smooth function is a 0-form. So a scalar field, such as $\phi(x, y, z)$, is also a 0-form.

3.2 1-forms

In $\mathbb{R}^3$, in general coordinates, every vector field can be associated with a corresponding 1-form and a corresponding 2-form. How does that work? For non-Cartesian coordinates we need something called a metric tensor g_{ij}, a type of function that measures infinitesimal distances on a manifold. The metric tensor encodes information about both the curvature of the manifold and the chosen coordinate system, and also allows us to convert vector components to 1-form components and vice versa.

However, in Cartesian coordinates, things are much simpler; the metric tensor is effectively just a collection of ones and zeros and the correspondences couldn't be more straightforward.

For 1-forms:
$$dx \Leftrightarrow \hat{\mathbf{e}}_x, \ dy \Leftrightarrow \hat{\mathbf{e}}_y, \ dz \Leftrightarrow \hat{\mathbf{e}}_z. \tag{3.2.1}$$

So a vector field
$$\mathbf{w}(x, y, z) = f_1 \hat{\mathbf{e}}_x + f_2 \hat{\mathbf{e}}_y + f_3 \hat{\mathbf{e}}_z$$

is associated with the 1-form

$$\omega_1 = f_1 \, dx + f_2 \, dy + f_3 \, dz. \tag{3.2.2}$$

In other words, we can regard the basis 1-forms as equivalent to the standard basis vectors, as illustrated in Figure 3.1.

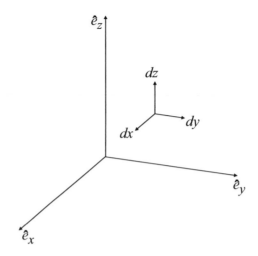

Figure 3.1: Basis 1-forms in Cartesian coordinates.

3.3 2-forms

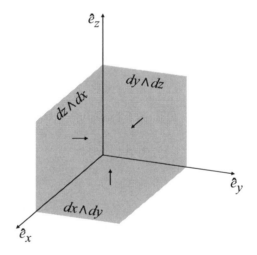

Figure 3.2: Basis 2-forms in Cartesian coordinates.

For 2-forms:

$$dy \wedge dz \Leftrightarrow \hat{\mathbf{e}}_x, \; dz \wedge dx \Leftrightarrow \hat{\mathbf{e}}_y, \; dx \wedge dy \Leftrightarrow \hat{\mathbf{e}}_z. \tag{3.3.1}$$

So a vector field

$$\mathbf{w}\left(x, y, z\right) = f_1 \hat{\mathbf{e}}_x + f_2 \hat{\mathbf{e}}_y + f_3 \hat{\mathbf{e}}_z$$

is also associated with the 2-form

$$\omega_2 = f_1 \, dy \wedge dz + f_2 \, dz \wedge dx + f_3 \, dx \wedge dy. \tag{3.3.2}$$

The basis 2-forms $dy \wedge dz$, $dz \wedge dx$ and $dx \wedge dy$ are equivalent to the standard unit basis vectors, but in a surfacey sort of way, as indicated in Figure 3.2. We can regard $dy \wedge dz$, $dz \wedge dx$ and $dx \wedge dy$ as flux-calculators that tell us how much fluid or field flows through surfaces aligned with the coordinate axes. To justify this flux interpretation of a 2-form, consider two vectors, $\mathbf{u}$ and $\mathbf{v}$, that span an oriented parallelogram P. Equation (2.3.4) tells us

$$\omega_2 \left(\mathbf{u}, \mathbf{v} \right) = \begin{vmatrix} f_1 & u^1 & v^1 \\ f_2 & u^2 & v^2 \\ f_3 & u^3 & v^3 \end{vmatrix} = \mathbf{w} \cdot \left(\mathbf{u} \times \mathbf{v} \right).$$

If we let $\mathbf{n}$ be a unit vector normal to P (and in the same direction as $\mathbf{u} \times \mathbf{v}$), we can write

$$\omega_2 \left(\mathbf{u}, \mathbf{v} \right) = \begin{vmatrix} f_1 & u^1 & v^1 \\ f_2 & u^2 & v^2 \\ f_3 & u^3 & v^3 \end{vmatrix} = \left(\mathbf{w} \cdot \mathbf{n} \right) \left(\mathbf{n} \cdot \left(\mathbf{u} \times \mathbf{v} \right) \right)$$

$$= \left(\mathbf{w} \cdot \mathbf{n} \right) \left\| \mathbf{u} \times \mathbf{v} \right\|$$

(where $\left\| \mathbf{u} \times \mathbf{v} \right\|$ is the magnitude of the cross product $\mathbf{u} \times \mathbf{v}$)

$$= \left(\mathbf{w} \cdot \mathbf{n} \right) \times \text{area of } P, \tag{3.3.3}$$

which tells us the component of $\mathbf{w}$ in the normal direction passing through P. If $\mathbf{w}$ represents a constant fluid flow, then we just need (3.3.3) to find the amount of fluid passing through the parallelogram P per unit time, ie the flux. Otherwise, if $\mathbf{w}$ describes a varying fluid flow, we need to use the surface integral version of (3.3.3), as described in chapter 8.

3.4 3-forms

In chapter 5 we'll see that the 3-form (5.3.3)

$$\left(\frac{\partial f_1}{\partial x} + \frac{\partial f_2}{\partial y} + \frac{\partial f_3}{\partial z} \right) dx \wedge dy \wedge dz \tag{3.4.1}$$

is associated with the divergence of a vector field, which is the scalar field

$$\phi_1 \left(x, y, z \right) = \left(\frac{\partial f_1}{\partial x} + \frac{\partial f_2}{\partial y} + \frac{\partial f_3}{\partial z} \right).$$

We started this chapter by noting that a scalar field is a 0-form. We have now come full circle by seeing that, in $\mathbb{R}^3$, the 3-form (3.4.1) is also associated with a scalar field. Table 3.1 summarises the correspondence between differential forms and vector calculus in $\mathbb{R}^3$.

	Differential form	Field	
0-form	$\phi(x, y, z)$	scalar	$\phi(x, y, z)$
1-form	$f_1\, dx + f_2\, dy + f_3\, dz$	vector	$f_1\hat{\mathbf{e}}_x + f_2\hat{\mathbf{e}}_y + f_3\hat{\mathbf{e}}_z$
2-form	$f_1\, dy \wedge dz + f_2\, dz \wedge dx + f_3\, dx \wedge dy$	vector	$f_1\hat{\mathbf{e}}_x + f_2\hat{\mathbf{e}}_y + f_3\hat{\mathbf{e}}_z$
3-form	$\left(\frac{\partial f_1}{\partial x} + \frac{\partial f_2}{\partial y} + \frac{\partial f_3}{\partial z}\right) dx \wedge dy \wedge dz$	scalar	$\phi_1(x, y, z)$

Table 3.1: Correspondence between differential forms and scalar/vector fields.

4 Differentiation

We need to be able to differentiate differential forms. We do this using something called the exterior derivative, which generalises the derivative of smooth functions (aka 0-forms) and incorporates the quirky, sign-flipping behaviour of the wedge product. The exterior derivative operator d changes a k-form to a $(k+1)$-form according to these four rules:

1. d is a linear operator, ie for the differential k-forms ω and ν

$$d\left(a\omega + b\nu\right) = a\,d\omega + b\,d\nu,$$

   where a and b are real numbers.

2. The exterior derivative of a 0-form (ie a smooth function) is the differential (2.2.1) that we've already met. So, for a function f in a space M with coordinates $x^1, \ldots, x^n$,

$$df = \frac{\partial f}{\partial x^1}dx^1 + \frac{\partial f}{\partial x^2}dx^2 + \ldots + \frac{\partial f}{\partial x^n}dx^n.$$

3. If ω is a p-form and ν is a q-form, then (this corresponds to the product rule of ordinary calculus)

$$d\left(\omega \wedge \nu\right) = d\omega \wedge \nu + (-1)^p\,\omega \wedge d\nu.$$

4. $d\left(d\omega\right) = 0$. Or, more succinctly, $dd = 0$.

A few examples in $\mathbb{R}^3$ should make the process clearer.

Example 4.1. For a function $f\left(x, y, z\right)$, find the exterior derivative of the 1-form df.

Rule 4, $d\left(d\omega\right) = 0$ (in this case $d\left(df\right) = 0$) tells us that the answer must be zero. However, it's instructive to see how that result inexorably emerges out of the calculation.

The derivative of f is given by rule 2, ie

$$df = \frac{\partial f}{\partial x}dx + \frac{\partial f}{\partial y}dy + \frac{\partial f}{\partial z}dz,$$

which is, of course, a 1-form. Taking the exterior derivative gives

$$d\left(df\right) = d\left(\frac{\partial f}{\partial x}dx + \frac{\partial f}{\partial y}dy + \frac{\partial f}{\partial z}dz\right)$$

61

$$= \frac{\partial^2 f}{\partial x \partial x} dx \wedge dx + \frac{\partial^2 f}{\partial y \partial x} dy \wedge dx + \frac{\partial^2 f}{\partial z \partial x} dz \wedge dx$$
$$+ \frac{\partial^2 f}{\partial x \partial y} dx \wedge dy + \frac{\partial^2 f}{\partial y \partial y} dy \wedge dy + \frac{\partial^2 f}{\partial z \partial y} dz \wedge dy$$
$$+ \frac{\partial^2 f}{\partial x \partial z} dx \wedge dz + \frac{\partial^2 f}{\partial y \partial z} dy \wedge dz + \frac{\partial^2 f}{\partial z \partial z} dz \wedge dz$$

$$= \frac{\partial^2 f}{\partial y \partial x} dy \wedge dx + \frac{\partial^2 f}{\partial z \partial x} dz \wedge dx$$
$$+ \frac{\partial^2 f}{\partial x \partial y} dx \wedge dy + \frac{\partial^2 f}{\partial z \partial y} dz \wedge dy$$
$$+ \frac{\partial^2 f}{\partial x \partial z} dx \wedge dz + \frac{\partial^2 f}{\partial y \partial z} dy \wedge dz.$$

Which we can rewrite, with the differentials in the correct orders, as

$$d\left(df\right) = \left(\frac{\partial^2 f}{\partial y \partial z} - \frac{\partial^2 f}{\partial z \partial y} \right) dy \wedge dz$$
$$+ \left(\frac{\partial^2 f}{\partial z \partial x} - \frac{\partial^2 f}{\partial x \partial z} \right) dz \wedge dx$$
$$+ \left(\frac{\partial^2 f}{\partial x \partial y} - \frac{\partial^2 f}{\partial y \partial x} \right) dx \wedge dy.$$

But partial derivatives commutes, ie $\frac{\partial^2 f}{\partial x \partial y} = \frac{\partial^2 f}{\partial y \partial x}$. Therefore

$$\left(\frac{\partial^2 f}{\partial y \partial z} - \frac{\partial^2 f}{\partial z \partial y} \right) = \left(\frac{\partial^2 f}{\partial z \partial x} - \frac{\partial^2 f}{\partial x \partial z} \right) = \left(\frac{\partial^2 f}{\partial x \partial y} - \frac{\partial^2 f}{\partial y \partial x} \right) = 0,$$

and we find

$$d\left(df\right) = 0,$$

which is what rule 4 tells us.

In passing, it's worth noting that a differential form ω is said to be closed if $d\omega = 0$.

Example 4.2. (a) Find $d\left(f\, dx\right)$ for a function $f\left(x, y, z\right)$. (b) Find $d\left(f\, dy\right)$ for $f\left(x, y, z\right) = x^3 y^2 z^4$; in other words, find the exterior derivative of the 1-form $x^3 y^2 z^4 dy$.

(a) Recall from section 2.3.1 that the convention is not to use the $\wedge$ when multiplying a form by a function, ie to write $f\, dx$ and not $f \wedge dx$. A function is a 0-form, so using rule 3 (with $p = 0$) we get

$$d\left(f \wedge dx\right) = d\left(f\, dx\right) = df \wedge dx + (-1)^0 f \wedge d\left(dx\right)$$

$$= df \wedge dx + 1 \times f \wedge 0$$
$$= df \wedge dx,$$

where we've also used rule 4, $d\left(dx\right) = 0$.

(b) Using this result we can write

$$d\left(f\, dy\right) = df \wedge dy,$$

which gives

$$d\left(x^3 y^2 z^4 dy\right) = \left(3x^2 y^2 z^4 dx + 2x^3 yz^4 dy + 4x^3 y^2 z^3 dz\right) \wedge dy$$
$$= 3x^2 y^2 z^4 dx \wedge dy - 4x^3 y^2 z^3 dy \wedge dz.$$

Note that $2x^3 yz^4 dy \wedge dy = 0$ because $dy \wedge dy = 0$. And we've changed the sign of the $4x^3 y^2 z^3 dz \wedge dy$ term to get the differentials dy, dz in the correct order. Note also that we start with a 1-form and finish with a 2-form.

Example 4.3. From Bryan [7]. Find $d\eta$ for the 2-form $\eta = \left(x + z^2\right) dx \wedge dy$.

We use rule 3 with $\omega = \left(x + z^2\right) dx$ and $\nu = dy$. As ω is a 1-form, $p = 1$ and we get

$$d\eta = d\left(\left(x + z^2\right) dx\right) \wedge dy + \left(-1\right)^1 \left(x + z^2\right) dx \wedge d\left(dy\right)$$
$$= \left(dx + 2z\, dz\right) \wedge dx \wedge dy - \left(x + z^2\right) dx \times 0$$
$$= 2z\, dz \wedge dx \wedge dy$$
$$= -2z\, dx \wedge dz \wedge dy$$
$$= 2z\, dx \wedge dy \wedge dz.$$

Note that we start with a 2-form and finish with a 3-form.

When looking at the wedge product in section 2.3.1 we saw that, because of (2.3.1)

$$dx^i \wedge dx^i = 0,$$

there are no 4-forms or higher in $\mathbb{R}^3$. So what happens if we try to sneak in a 4-form by taking the exterior derivative of a 3-form in $\mathbb{R}^3$?

Example 4.4. Find $d\left(f\, dx \wedge dy \wedge dz\right)$ for a function $f\left(x, y, z\right)$.

We use rule 3 with $\omega = f\, dx$ and $\nu = dy \wedge dz$. ω is a 1-form, so $p = 1$, and we get

$$d\left(f\, dx \wedge dy \wedge dz\right) = d\left(f\, dx\right) \wedge dy \wedge dz + \left(-1\right)^1 \left(f\, dx\right) \wedge d\left(dy \wedge dz\right)$$
$$= df \wedge dx \wedge dy \wedge dz$$
$$= \left(\frac{\partial f}{\partial x} dx + \frac{\partial f}{\partial y} dy + \frac{\partial f}{\partial z} dz\right) \wedge dx \wedge dy \wedge dz$$
$$= 0,$$

because $dx \wedge dx = dy \wedge dy = dz \wedge dz = 0$. Which is what we'd expect – in $\mathbb{R}^3$ the exterior derivative of a 3-form is zero.

5 Div, grad and curl

There are four kinds of differential forms in $\mathbb{R}^3$: 0-forms, 1-forms, 2-forms and 3-forms. We've just seen that in $\mathbb{R}^3$ the exterior derivative of a 3-form vanishes. By taking the exterior derivative of 0-forms, 1-forms and 2-forms we can express the three important operators of vector calculus – grad, curl and div – in the language of differential forms.

5.1 Gradient and 0-forms

The gradient (written grad f or ∇f) of a scalar field $f(x, y, z)$ is a vector field that tells us two things. First, at any point, the gradient vector points in the direction of greatest rate of increase of f. Second, the magnitude of the gradient vector gives the rate of increase of f in that direction. The gradient of a scalar field $f(x, y, z)$ is given by

$$\operatorname{grad} f = \nabla f = \frac{\partial f}{\partial x}\hat{\mathbf{e}}_x + \frac{\partial f}{\partial y}\hat{\mathbf{e}}_y + \frac{\partial f}{\partial z}\hat{\mathbf{e}}_z. \tag{5.1.1}$$

Using the correspondence (3.2.1)

$$dx \Leftrightarrow \hat{\mathbf{e}}_x,\ dy \Leftrightarrow \hat{\mathbf{e}}_y,\ dz \Leftrightarrow \hat{\mathbf{e}}_z,$$

this gradient vector field can be associated with the exterior derivative of the 0-form $f(x, y, z)$, which is the 1-form

$$df = \frac{\partial f}{\partial x}dx + \frac{\partial f}{\partial y}dy + \frac{\partial f}{\partial z}dz.$$

5.2 Curl and 1-forms

The curl (written curl $\mathbf{v}$ or $\nabla \times \mathbf{v}$) of a vector field $\mathbf{v}$ is itself a vector and is a measure of the field's rotation at a point. Let the vector field represent the flow of some fluid. Now imagine inserting a tiny sphere into the fluid. The sphere is ingeniously secured in such a way that it isn't carried along with the fluid's current but is free to rotate in any direction. The rotation of the sphere is a measure of the curl of the vector field; no rotation, means zero curl. The direction of the vector curl $\mathbf{v}$ is along the sphere's axis of rotation, as determined by the right-hand rule. Curl the fingers of your right hand in the direction of the sphere's rotation with your thumb perpendicular to your fist. Your thumb is then pointing in the direction of curl $\mathbf{v}$.

The curl of a vector field $\mathbf{v}\,(x,y,z) = f_1\hat{\mathbf{e}}_x + f_2\hat{\mathbf{e}}_y + f_3\hat{\mathbf{e}}_z$ is given by

$$\text{curl}\,\mathbf{v} = \nabla \times \mathbf{v} = \left(\frac{\partial f_3}{\partial y} - \frac{\partial f_2}{\partial z}\right)\hat{\mathbf{e}}_x + \left(\frac{\partial f_1}{\partial z} - \frac{\partial f_3}{\partial x}\right)\hat{\mathbf{e}}_y + \left(\frac{\partial f_2}{\partial x} - \frac{\partial f_1}{\partial y}\right)\hat{\mathbf{e}}_z, \quad (5.2.1)$$

or, in determinant form,

$$\text{curl}\,\mathbf{v} = \begin{vmatrix} \hat{\mathbf{e}}_x & \hat{\mathbf{e}}_y & \hat{\mathbf{e}}_z \\ \frac{\partial}{\partial x} & \frac{\partial}{\partial y} & \frac{\partial}{\partial z} \\ f_1 & f_2 & f_3 \end{vmatrix}.$$

Now let's take the exterior derivative of the 1-form (3.2.2) associated with $\mathbf{v}\,(x,y,z)$:

$$\omega_1 = f_1\,dx + f_2\,dy + f_3\,dz,$$

to get

$$d\omega_1 = d\,(f_1\,dx + f_2\,dy + f_3\,dz) \qquad\qquad (5.2.2)$$

$$= df_1 \wedge dx + df_2 \wedge dy + df_3 \wedge dz$$

$$= \left(\frac{\partial f_1}{\partial x}dx + \frac{\partial f_1}{\partial y}dy + \frac{\partial f_1}{\partial z}dz\right) \wedge dx$$

$$+ \left(\frac{\partial f_2}{\partial x}dx + \frac{\partial f_2}{\partial y}dy + \frac{\partial f_2}{\partial z}dz\right) \wedge dy$$

$$+ \left(\frac{\partial f_3}{\partial x}dx + \frac{\partial f_3}{\partial y}dy + \frac{\partial f_3}{\partial z}dz\right) \wedge dz$$

$$= \frac{\partial f_1}{\partial y}dy \wedge dx + \frac{\partial f_1}{\partial z}dz \wedge dx$$

$$+ \frac{\partial f_2}{\partial x}dx \wedge dy + \frac{\partial f_2}{\partial z}dz \wedge dy$$

$$+ \frac{\partial f_3}{\partial x}dx \wedge dz + \frac{\partial f_3}{\partial y}dy \wedge dz$$

$$= \left(\frac{\partial f_3}{\partial y} - \frac{\partial f_2}{\partial z}\right)dy \wedge dz + \left(\frac{\partial f_1}{\partial z} - \frac{\partial f_3}{\partial x}\right)dz \wedge dx + \left(\frac{\partial f_2}{\partial x} - \frac{\partial f_1}{\partial y}\right)dx \wedge dy,$$

where we've changed the signs to get the differentials in the correct order and used $dx^i \wedge dx^i = 0$.

If we use the correspondence (3.3.1)

$$dy \wedge dz \Leftrightarrow \hat{\mathbf{e}}_x, \; dz \wedge dx \Leftrightarrow \hat{\mathbf{e}}_y, \; dx \wedge dy \Leftrightarrow \hat{\mathbf{e}}_z,$$

we can nicely associate the exterior derivative $d\omega_1$ with the equation for curl (5.2.1).

5.3 Divergence and 2-forms

The divergence (written $\operatorname{div} \mathbf{w}$ or $\nabla \cdot \mathbf{w}$) of a vector field $\mathbf{w}$ is a scalar field and is a measure of the net flow of fluid through an infinitesimally small closed surface surrounding a point. If more fluid is leaving than entering the surface, the point is a source (think of a running tap as a source of water) and the divergence is positive. If more fluid is entering than leaving the surface, the point is a sink (think of water flowing down a drain) and the divergence is negative. If the same amount of fluid is entering as leaving, there is zero divergence.

The divergence of a vector field $\mathbf{w}(x, y, z) = f_1 \hat{\mathbf{e}}_x + f_2 \hat{\mathbf{e}}_y + f_3 \hat{\mathbf{e}}_z$ is given by

$$\operatorname{div} \mathbf{w} = \nabla \cdot \mathbf{w} = \frac{\partial f_1}{\partial x} + \frac{\partial f_2}{\partial y} + \frac{\partial f_3}{\partial z}. \tag{5.3.1}$$

If we take the exterior derivative of the 2-form (3.3.2) associated with $\mathbf{w}(x, y, z)$:

$$\omega_2 = f_1 \, dy \wedge dz + f_2 \, dz \wedge dx + f_3 \, dx \wedge dy,$$

we get

$$d\omega_2 = d\left(f_1 \, dy \wedge dz + f_2 \, dz \wedge dx + f_3 \, dx \wedge dy\right) \tag{5.3.2}$$

$$= df_1 \wedge dy \wedge dz + df_2 \wedge dz \wedge dx + df_3 \wedge dx \wedge dy$$

$$= \frac{\partial f_1}{\partial x} dx \wedge dy \wedge dz + \frac{\partial f_2}{\partial y} dy \wedge dz \wedge dx + \frac{\partial f_3}{\partial z} dz \wedge dx \wedge dy$$

$$= \left(\frac{\partial f_1}{\partial x} + \frac{\partial f_2}{\partial y} + \frac{\partial f_3}{\partial z}\right) dx \wedge dy \wedge dz. \tag{5.3.3}$$

The coefficient of this 3-form is the scalar field

$$\left(\frac{\partial f_1}{\partial x} + \frac{\partial f_2}{\partial y} + \frac{\partial f_3}{\partial z}\right),$$

which is the equation for divergence (5.3.1). So we can associate the exterior derivative $d\omega_2$ with the divergence $\nabla \cdot \mathbf{v}$.

Table 5.1 summarises the relationships between the vector calculus operators grad, curl and div and their associated differential forms.

	scalar field			vector fields			vector fields			scalar field
vector calculus	f	$\xrightarrow{\text{grad}}$	∇f	$\mathbf{v}$	$\xrightarrow{\text{curl}}$	$\nabla \times \mathbf{v}$	$\mathbf{w}$	$\xrightarrow{\text{div}}$	$\nabla \cdot \mathbf{w}$
	$\updownarrow$		$\updownarrow$	$\updownarrow$		$\updownarrow$	$\updownarrow$		$\updownarrow$
differential forms	f 0-form	$\xrightarrow{d}$	df 1-form	ω_1 1-form	$\xrightarrow{d}$	$d\omega_1$ 2-form	ω_2 2-form	$\xrightarrow{d}$	$d\omega_2$ 3-form

Table 5.1: Grad, curl and div with vector calculus and differential forms.

5.4 A couple of vector identities

In chapter 4 we saw that rule 4 for taking the exterior derivative is $d(d\omega) = 0$. We can use this rule to easily obtain two important vector calculus identities.

First, recall that if we take the exterior derivative of the 1-form

$$\omega_1 = f_1\,dx + f_2\,dy + f_3\,dz$$

associated with the vector field $\mathbf{v}(x, y, z)$, we get (5.2.2)

$$d\omega_1 = d(f_1\,dx + f_2\,dy + f_3\,dz),$$

which corresponds to curl $\mathbf{v} = \nabla \times \mathbf{v}$. Now substitute for ω_1 the 1-form df, which can be associated with the gradient vector field

$$\text{grad } f = \nabla f = \frac{\partial f}{\partial x}\hat{\mathbf{e}}_x + \frac{\partial f}{\partial y}\hat{\mathbf{e}}_y + \frac{\partial f}{\partial z}\hat{\mathbf{e}}_z.$$

But $d(df) = 0$.

- This tells us that

$$\nabla \times \nabla f = 0,$$

  ie the curl of the gradient is zero.

Second, recall that if we take the exterior derivative of the 2-form

$$\omega_2 = f_1\,dy \wedge dz + f_2\,dz \wedge dx + f_3\,dx \wedge dy$$

associated with the vector field $\mathbf{w}(x, y, z)$, we get (5.3.2)

$$d\omega_2 = d(f_1\,dy \wedge dz + f_2\,dz \wedge dx + f_3\,dx \wedge dy),$$

the coefficient of which,

$$\left(\frac{\partial f_1}{\partial x} + \frac{\partial f_2}{\partial y} + \frac{\partial f_3}{\partial z}\right),$$

corresponds to the divergence $\nabla \cdot \mathbf{w}$. Now substitute for ω_2 the 2-form $d\omega_1$, which can be associated with the curl vector field

$$\text{curl } \mathbf{v} = \nabla \times \mathbf{v} = \left(\frac{\partial f_3}{\partial y} - \frac{\partial f_2}{\partial z}\right)\hat{\mathbf{e}}_x + \left(\frac{\partial f_1}{\partial z} - \frac{\partial f_3}{\partial x}\right)\hat{\mathbf{e}}_y + \left(\frac{\partial f_2}{\partial x} - \frac{\partial f_1}{\partial y}\right)\hat{\mathbf{e}}_z.$$

But $d(d\omega_1) = 0$.

- This tells us that

$$\nabla \cdot (\nabla \times \mathbf{v}) = 0,$$

  ie the divergence of the curl is zero.

6 Orientation

We'll see in the next chapter that we integrate differential k-forms over *oriented k-manifolds* (a 1-form over a one-dimensional curve, for example), so we need to look at the notion of orientation. A manifold that is orientable has one of two orientations. We can think of orientation as one of two non-equivalent ways in which objects are situated in space. Intuitively, a change of orientation describes the difference between a page of text and its mirror image; each being a reflection of the other. We could arbitrarily label these two orientations 'ordinary' and 'mirror'. No matter how much we might rotate or stretch the page of text, we won't be able to change its orientation from 'ordinary' to 'mirror'. Only a reflection can do that.

- The key practical point when doing calculations is that if we muddle up the orientation our answer may end up with the wrong sign.

We'll begin by considering the orientation of a vector space, namely the basis vectors of $\mathbb{R}^n$. First, geometrically, for $\mathbb{R}^1, \mathbb{R}^2$ and $\mathbb{R}^3$, then progressing to a more general algebraic analysis for $\mathbb{R}^n$.

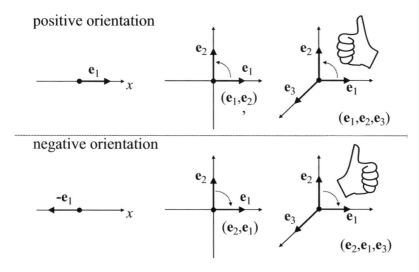

Figure 6.1: Oriented bases for $\mathbb{R}^1, \mathbb{R}^2$ and $\mathbb{R}^3$.

A geometric interpretation of basis orientation is shown in Figure 6.1, which depicts positive and negative oriented bases for $\mathbb{R}^1, \mathbb{R}^2$ and $\mathbb{R}^3$. (Note that labelling an orientation 'positive' or 'negative' is completely arbitrary, a matter of convention, not mathematical fact.) The top row shows the standard or preferred orientations. In $\mathbb{R}^1$ the standard (positive) orientation is given by the basis vector $\mathbf{e}_1$ pointing to the right (ie in the direction of increasing x). In $\mathbb{R}^2$ the standard (positive or counterclockwise) orientation is given by noting that the shortest path from the first basis vector $\mathbf{e}_1$ to the second basis vector $\mathbf{e}_2$ is in a counterclockwise direction. In $\mathbb{R}^3$ the standard (positive or right-handed) orientation is given using the right-hand rule, which states that if you hold your right hand so that the fingers curl from $\mathbf{e}_1$ to $\mathbf{e}_2$, your thumb will be pointing in the direction of $\mathbf{e}_3$. (Alternatively, imagine looking down the $\mathbf{e}_3$ vector; the shortest path from $\mathbf{e}_1$ to $\mathbf{e}_2$ is then in a counterclockwise direction.)

The bottom row shows the corresponding opposite orientations. In $\mathbb{R}^1$ the negative orientation is given by the basis vector $-\mathbf{e}_1$ pointing to the left (ie in the direction of decreasing x). In $\mathbb{R}^2$ we now make $\mathbf{e}_2$ the first basis vector. The (negative or clockwise) orientation is given by noting that the shortest path from $\mathbf{e}_2$ to $\mathbf{e}_1$ is in a clockwise direction. In $\mathbb{R}^3$ we also now make $\mathbf{e}_2$ the first basis vector and $\mathbf{e}_1$ the second basis vector. The (negative or left-handed) orientation is given using the left-hand rule, which states that if you hold your left hand so that the fingers curl from $\mathbf{e}_2$ to $\mathbf{e}_1$, your thumb will be pointing in the direction of $\mathbf{e}_3$. (Alternatively, imagine looking down the $\mathbf{e}_3$ vector; the shortest path from $\mathbf{e}_2$ to $\mathbf{e}_1$ is then in a clockwise direction.)

Descriptions such as 'to the right', 'to the left', 'counterclockwise', 'clockwise', 'right-handed' and 'left-handed' are somewhat vague. What would counterclockwise mean, for example, if we were trying to understand the orientation of $\mathbb{R}^n$ where $n > 3$? To put things on a precise, mathematical footing, we introduce an algebraic interpretation of orientation. We do this by specifying an orientation for $\mathbb{R}^n$ using an ordered basis $(\mathbf{e}_1, \ldots, \mathbf{e}_n)$. We've already implicitly made use of ordered bases when we referred to rules for finding the shortest path (counterclockwise or clockwise) from the first to the second basis vectors. In effect, we were saying that for a standard positive orientation, the ordered bases for $\mathbb{R}^2$ and $\mathbb{R}^3$ are, respectively, $(\mathbf{e}_1, \mathbf{e}_2)$ and $(\mathbf{e}_1, \mathbf{e}_2, \mathbf{e}_3)$. And, for a negative orientation, the ordered bases for $\mathbb{R}^2$ and $\mathbb{R}^3$ are $(\mathbf{e}_2, \mathbf{e}_1)$ and $(\mathbf{e}_2, \mathbf{e}_1, \mathbf{e}_3)$. We saw that if we swapped any two vectors in an ordered basis the orientation flips. For example, the orientation in $\mathbb{R}^2$ changes from positive to negative if we change the ordered basis from $(\mathbf{e}_1, \mathbf{e}_2)$ to $(\mathbf{e}_2, \mathbf{e}_1)$. You should be able to see that the orientation also flips if we change the sign of any basis vector. So, referring to the top row, middle diagram in Figure 6.1, if we changed the sign of $\mathbf{e}_1$, the vector would be pointing from the origin to the left, the shortest path from $\mathbf{e}_1$ to $\mathbf{e}_2$ would be in a clockwise direction and the orientation would change from positive to negative.

Objects that are (a) assembled from vectors, (b) change sign if any two vectors are swapped, and (c) change sign if any one vector is multiplied by -1 may well sound familiar. These, of course, are properties of the determinant. In fact, determinants are the key to deciding whether two ordered bases in $\mathbb{R}^n$ have the same orientation, which they do if their determinants have the same sign. We can see what this means by assuming the vectors in Figure 6.1 are orthonormal unit basis vectors. We then have:

$$\det(\mathbf{e}_1) = |1| = 1, \quad \det(-\mathbf{e}_1) = |-1| = -1,$$

$$\det\left(\mathbf{e}_1,\mathbf{e}_2\right) = \begin{vmatrix} 1 & 0 \\ 0 & 1 \end{vmatrix} = 1, \quad \det\left(\mathbf{e}_2,\mathbf{e}_1\right) = \begin{vmatrix} 0 & 1 \\ 1 & 0 \end{vmatrix} = -1,$$

$$\det\left(\mathbf{e}_1,\mathbf{e}_2,\mathbf{e}_3\right) = \begin{vmatrix} 1 & 0 & 0 \\ 0 & 1 & 0 \\ 0 & 0 & 1 \end{vmatrix} = 1, \quad \det\left(\mathbf{e}_2,\mathbf{e}_1,\mathbf{e}_3\right) = \begin{vmatrix} 0 & 1 & 0 \\ 1 & 0 & 0 \\ 0 & 0 & 1 \end{vmatrix} = -1.$$

The positively oriented bases on the left have positive determinants. The negatively oriented bases on the right have negative determinants. And this analysis also works for non-orthonormal ordered bases in $\mathbb{R}^n$. So if we have two ordered bases $(\mathbf{u}_1,\ldots,\mathbf{u}_n)$ and $(\mathbf{v}_1,\ldots,\mathbf{v}_n)$, and the determinant of both has the same sign, then both bases have the same orientation. For example, assume that in $\mathbb{R}^4$ an ordered basis $(\mathbf{e}_1,\mathbf{e}_2,\mathbf{e}_3,\mathbf{e}_4)$ is given by $\mathbf{e}_1 = (1,3,2,0)$, $\mathbf{e}_2 = (2,2,1,3)$, $\mathbf{e}_3 = (3,1,3,-2)$ and $\mathbf{e}_4 = (1,-1,3,3)$. If we write these basis vectors out as a 4×4 matrix, we find the determinant to be -128. Any other ordered basis in $\mathbb{R}^4$ with a negative determinant also has the same orientation as $(\mathbf{e}_1,\mathbf{e}_2,\mathbf{e}_3,\mathbf{e}_4)$.

For any vector space (not just $\mathbb{R}^n$), if we have two ordered bases $E = (\mathbf{u}_1,\ldots,\mathbf{u}_n)$ and $E' = (\mathbf{v}_1,\ldots,\mathbf{v}_n)$ and a change-of-basis matrix A that transforms E' to E, we can write the matrix equation

$$E = AE'.$$

E and E' then have the same orientation if the determinant of A is positive.

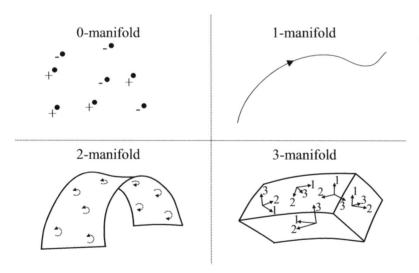

Figure 6.2: Orientation of manifolds.

Moving on from orientations of vector spaces – how do we decide the orientation of a manifold? We won't delve into the mathematical details, but instead give a (very) basic overview. Figure 6.2 (from Penrose [17]) illustrates the orientations of four different manifolds. A 0-manifold (0-dimensional manifold) is a set of discrete points.

An orientation on a 0-manifold is a choice of sign, positive $(+)$ or negative $(-)$, for each point. The orientation of a 1-manifold (one-dimensional manifold), or curve, is a choice of direction by which we move along the curve. The orientation of a 2-manifold can be illustrated using little circles showing the rotation of tangent vectors at a point in a 'positive' direction. In the words of Penrose: 'For a 3-manifold the orientation specifies which triad of independent vectors at a point is to be regarded as "right-handed" and which as "left-handed".'

Recall that we earlier noted that the tangent space is a vector space. Put simply, if all the tangent spaces on a manifold can be oriented consistently, we say the manifold is orientable. We've just seen that the orientation of an n-dimensional vector space can be understood in terms of the sign of an $n \times n$ determinant. We know that an $n \times n$ determinant is a multilinear alternating function of n vectors (written as columns or rows). We also know that a differential n-form is a linear or, more generally, multilinear alternating function of n tangent vectors. It shouldn't come as a great surprise, therefore, that differential n-forms are involved in the concept of manifold orientation. The idea, which at our level we don't use but is worth mentioning in passing, is that an n-dimensional manifold M is orientable if and only if there exists on M a nowhere-zero differential n-form. For example, the 2-form $dx \wedge dy$ is nowhere-zero on $\mathbb{R}^2$, therefore $\mathbb{R}^2$ is orientable. Fortney [9] states:

> Thus the set of all nowhere-zero n-forms splits into two equivalence classes, one equivalence class that consists of all the everywhere positive nowhere-zero n-forms and a second equivalence class that consists of all the every-where negative nowhere-zero n-forms. By choosing one of these two equivalence classes we are specifying what is called an orientation of the manifold.

Now let's return to earth and take a more practical look at orientation with reference to the elementary manifolds we are concerned with in this book. The orientation of a parameterised curve is usually taken to be in the direction of increasing values of the parameter. An ordinary two-sided surface in $\mathbb{R}^3$ will, at every point, have two unit normal vectors $\mathbf{n}$ and $-\mathbf{n}$, each pointing in opposite directions. The surface of a sphere, for example, will have unit normal vectors pointing inwards and outwards. We give the surface an orientation by choosing one of these two sets of unit normal vectors. Not all surfaces are orientable. The Möbius strip, for example, is a one-sided surface and therefore not orientable.

There are various ad hoc rules that reflect the standard right-handed orientation of $\mathbb{R}^3$. The right-hand rule used for the cross-product, for example. Green's theorem only works (without a change of sign) when the boundary curve has a positive orientation if it is traced out in a counterclockwise direction. Stokes' theorem involves a surface S with boundary curve C. The orientation of S (determined by the choice of normal vector $\mathbf{n}$) must match the orientation of the boundary C. The rule is that the direction of C is considered positive if you are walking around C with your head pointing in the direction of $\mathbf{n}$ and the surface is on your left.

- The good news as far as we're concerned is that almost all the manifolds we encounter in this book are described parametrically. When we parameterise a manifold M, that parameterisation will induce an orientation on M. This induced orientation is the one we'll be using.

Finally, one aspect of orientation that we must take on board with regard to differential forms is the necessity of keeping the differentials in the correct order (so that the sign comes out right). For example, the standard positive orientation built into $\mathbb{R}^2$ means the correct order of dx, dy is

$$dx \wedge dy.$$

And the standard right-handed orientation built into $\mathbb{R}^3$ means the correct order of dx, dy and dz is

$$dx \wedge dy \wedge dz.$$

Of course, we're not confined to $\mathbb{R}^3$. Say we have an n-form in $\mathbb{R}^n$ with coordinates $u^1, u^2, \ldots, u^n$. By choosing an order for the coordinates, we choose an orientation for our $\mathbb{R}^n$ space. If we choose the obvious order $u^1, u^2, \ldots, u^n$, the correct order of $du^1, du^2, \ldots, du^n$ is straightforward:

$$du^1 \wedge du^2 \cdots \wedge du^n.$$

Interchanging any two of the du^i differentials introduces a minus sign (due to the anti-commutativity of the wedge product) and therefore puts the thing in the wrong order. So, for example,

$$du^2 \wedge du^1 \cdots \wedge du^n$$

is in incorrect order, because

$$du^2 \wedge du^1 \cdots \wedge du^n = -du^1 \wedge du^2 \cdots \wedge du^n.$$

Assuming it has one, an n-dimensional manifold M has a boundary ∂M of dimension $n - 1$. If you ever need to integrate over a boundary, you will need an n-1 differential form. It's therefore instructive to understand the correct order (with du^i omitted) for $(n-1)$-forms. This one isn't quite so straightforward. Here it is:

$$(-1)^{(i-1)} du^1 \cdots \wedge du^{(i-1)} \wedge du^{(i+1)} \cdots \wedge du^n. \qquad (6.0.1)$$

We'll do a quick example before justifying this formula.

Example 6.1. From Parkinson [15]. We have a 5-form $\omega = du^1 \wedge du^2 \wedge du^3 \wedge du^4 \wedge du^5$ in $\mathbb{R}^5$. What is the correct order for a 4-form with (a) du^2 removed, and (b) du^3 removed.

(a) du^2 means $i = 2$, and (6.0.1) becomes

$$(-1)^{(2-1)} du^1 \wedge du^3 \wedge du^4 \wedge du^5$$
$$= (-1)^1 du^1 \wedge du^3 \wedge du^4 \wedge du^5$$
$$= -du^1 \wedge du^3 \wedge du^4 \wedge du^5.$$

(b) du^3 means $i = 3$, and (6.0.1) becomes

$$(-1)^{(3-1)} du^1 \wedge du^2 \wedge du^4 \wedge du^5$$
$$= (-1)^2 du^1 \wedge du^2 \wedge du^4 \wedge du^5$$
$$= du^1 \wedge du^2 \wedge du^4 \wedge du^5.$$

We can understand (6.0.1) by noting that

$$du^i \wedge (-1)^{(i-1)} \, du^1 \cdots \wedge du^{(i-1)} \wedge du^{(i+1)} \cdots \wedge du^n = du^1 \wedge du^2 \cdots \wedge du^n,$$

because the du^i has to jump over $i-1$ differentials until it gets back to its rightful place between $du^{(i-1)}$ and $du^{(i+1)}$, with each jump changing the sign of the expression.

Returning to $\mathbb{R}^3$, the correct order for the basis 2-forms is

$$dy \wedge dz, \ -dx \wedge dz, \ dx \wedge dy,$$

which we can rewrite as

$$dy \wedge dz, \ dz \wedge dx, \ dx \wedge dy.$$

7 Integrating differential forms

Differential forms are the answer to the question: what objects do we integrate on manifolds? When we first learned calculus, we might have been told we were integrating functions, but actually we weren't. For $y = f(x)$, we didn't find

$$\int f(x),$$

ie the integral of a function. Instead, we found

$$\int f(x)\, dx,$$

the integral of the 1-form $f(x)\, dx$. The crucial thing about differential forms is that they allow us to do integration on manifolds in a coordinate-independent way.

For example, using x, y, z coordinates, say we have a $2 \times 2 \times 2$ cube D of mass m and constant density $m/8$ per unit volume. In other words, our cube has volume 8 and mass given by

$$\int_D \left(\frac{m}{8}\right) dx\, dy\, dz = \int_0^2 \int_0^2 \int_0^2 \left(\frac{m}{8}\right) dx\, dy\, dz = m.$$

Now, say we want to change to new coordinates u, v, w, where $u = \frac{3x}{2}$, $v = \frac{3y}{2}$ and $w = \frac{3z}{2}$. The same cube with the same mass, but now measured in u, v, w coordinates, has side length 3, volume 27, density $m/27$ per unit volume and mass given by

$$\int_D \left(\frac{m}{27}\right) du\, dv\, dw = \int_0^3 \int_0^3 \int_0^3 \left(\frac{m}{27}\right) du\, dv\, dw = m.$$

In the language of differential forms, we have a 3-form ω that tells us the density of our cube. We've expressed that 3-form in two coordinate systems, ie

$$\omega = \left(\frac{m}{8}\right) dx \wedge dy \wedge dz = \left(\frac{m}{27}\right) du \wedge dv \wedge dw.$$

We integrated ω by simply removing the wedges and then calculating an ordinary triple integral. In a coordinate independent fashion, the cube's mass m can be written as

$$m = \int_D \omega.$$

Differential forms are things that return a number after being integrated over an oriented portion of curve, surface or higher dimensional space. The essential rule when integrating differential forms is that:

- a differential k-form must be integrated over an oriented k-dimensional manifold. In other words, a 1-form is integrated over an oriented one-dimensional curve; a 2-form is integrated over an oriented two-dimensional surface; a 3-form is integrated over an oriented three-dimensional volume, and so on.

Bearing this rule in mind, we need to find a way of integrating a k-form ω over a k-dimensional manifold, M. As already indicated, we denote this integral as

$$\int_M \omega. \tag{7.0.1}$$

Note that this integral does not depend on how M is parameterised. We'll derive the independence of parameterisation for curves and surfaces in $\mathbb{R}^3$ at the end of this chapter.

If we are working in $\mathbb{R}^3$, M might be a parameterised three-dimensional curve C, ω would be a 1-form and (7.0.1) would be written as

$$\int_C \omega.$$

Or if M is a parameterised surface S, ω would be a 2-form and (7.0.1) would be written as

$$\int_S \omega.$$

So we need a working definition of (7.0.1). Actually, as we'll see, there are two definitions of (7.0.1):

- One for when a differential k-form is integrated over a k-dimensional manifold in $\mathbb{R}^n$, where $k < n$. For example, a 1-form integrated over a curve in $\mathbb{R}^3$.

- And a more straightforward version for when a differential n-form is integrated over an n-dimensional manifold in $\mathbb{R}^n$. For example, a 2-form integrated over a surface in $\mathbb{R}^2$.

The final step before stating and justifying these definitions is to use differential forms to derive the change of variables formula, which is what we'll now do.

7.1 Change of variables

If we want to integrate a 2-form $\omega = f(x, y) \, dx \wedge dy$ over a surface S, we have

$$\int_S \omega = \int_S f(x, y) \, dx \wedge dy.$$

Now, say we want to change to some new coordinates u, v (in some region D of the uv plane). The old x, y coordinates will be functions of the new u, v coordinates:

$$x = x(u, v),$$

$$y = y(u, v).$$

And we have

$$f(x, y) = f(x(u, v), y(u, v)),$$

where $f(x(u, v), y(u, v))$ is $f(x, y)$ in terms of u, v.

The differential dx is

$$dx = \frac{\partial x}{\partial u} du + \frac{\partial x}{\partial v} dv.$$

And the differential dy is

$$dy = \frac{\partial y}{\partial u} du + \frac{\partial y}{\partial v} dv.$$

And we can write $dx \wedge dy$ as

$$dx \wedge dy = \left(\frac{\partial x}{\partial u} du + \frac{\partial x}{\partial v} dv \right) \wedge \left(\frac{\partial y}{\partial u} du + \frac{\partial y}{\partial v} dv \right).$$

After multiplying out the brackets and remembering $du \wedge du = dv \wedge dv = 0$ and $du \wedge dv = -dv \wedge du$, we get

$$dx \wedge dy = \left(\frac{\partial x}{\partial u} \frac{\partial y}{\partial v} - \frac{\partial x}{\partial v} \frac{\partial y}{\partial u} \right) du \wedge dv$$

$$= \begin{vmatrix} \frac{\partial x}{\partial u} & \frac{\partial x}{\partial v} \\ \frac{\partial y}{\partial u} & \frac{\partial y}{\partial v} \end{vmatrix} du \wedge dv. \tag{7.1.1}$$

And therefore

$$\int_S f(x, y) \, dx \wedge dy = \int_D f(x(u, v), y(u, v)) \begin{vmatrix} \frac{\partial x}{\partial u} & \frac{\partial x}{\partial v} \\ \frac{\partial y}{\partial u} & \frac{\partial y}{\partial v} \end{vmatrix} du \wedge dv. \tag{7.1.2}$$

We can use

$$\det \left(\frac{\partial(x, y)}{\partial(u, v)} \right)$$

to denote

$$\begin{vmatrix} \frac{\partial x}{\partial u} & \frac{\partial x}{\partial v} \\ \frac{\partial y}{\partial u} & \frac{\partial y}{\partial v} \end{vmatrix},$$

where the matrix

$$\frac{\partial(x, y)}{\partial(u, v)} = \begin{bmatrix} \frac{\partial x}{\partial u} & \frac{\partial x}{\partial v} \\ \frac{\partial y}{\partial u} & \frac{\partial y}{\partial v} \end{bmatrix}$$

is the Jacobian matrix (previously encountered in the change of basis formulas in sections 2.2.4 and 2.2.6.2).

We can therefore write (7.1.2) as

$$\int_S f\left(x, y\right) dx \wedge dy = \int_D f\left(x\left(u, v\right), y\left(u, v\right)\right) \det\left(\frac{\partial\left(x, y\right)}{\partial\left(u, v\right)}\right) du \wedge dv,$$

or, more succinctly and with some abuse of notation, as

$$\int_S f\, dx \wedge dy = \int_D f\, \det\left(\frac{\partial\left(x, y\right)}{\partial\left(u, v\right)}\right) du \wedge dv.$$

If we assume that S and D have the same orientation, we can remove the wedges and change this into an ordinary (ie unoriented) double integral:

$$\int_S f\, dx \wedge dy = \int_S f\, dx\, dy = \int_D f\, \det\left(\frac{\partial\left(x, y\right)}{\partial\left(u, v\right)}\right) du\, dv. \qquad (7.1.3)$$

Otherwise, in order for the sign to come out right, we need to take the absolute value of the determinant to give

$$\int_S f\, dx\, dy = \int_D f\, \left|\det\left(\frac{\partial\left(x, y\right)}{\partial\left(u, v\right)}\right)\right| du\, dv. \qquad (7.1.4)$$

Think of the absolute value of the determinant as a scale factor that converts an infinitesimal $du\, dv$ area into an infinitesimal $dx\, dy$ area.

So if, for example, we were changing to polar coordinates, (7.1.4) would become

$$\int_S f\left(x, y\right) dx\, dy = \int_D f\left(x\left(r, \theta\right), y\left(r, \theta\right)\right) \left|\det\left(\frac{\partial\left(x, y\right)}{\partial\left(r, \theta\right)}\right)\right| dr\, d\theta. \qquad (7.1.5)$$

In polar coordinates, $x = r\cos\theta$ and $y = r\sin\theta$. The Jacobian determinant is therefore

$$\det\left(\frac{\partial\left(x, y\right)}{\partial\left(r, \theta\right)}\right) = \begin{vmatrix} \frac{\partial x}{\partial r} & \frac{\partial x}{\partial \theta} \\ \frac{\partial y}{\partial r} & \frac{\partial y}{\partial \theta} \end{vmatrix}$$

$$= \begin{vmatrix} \cos\theta & -r\sin\theta \\ \sin\theta & r\cos\theta \end{vmatrix}$$

$$= r\cos^2\theta - \left(-r\sin^2\theta\right)$$

$$= r\left(\cos^2\theta + \sin^2\theta\right)$$

$$= r.$$

So the change of variables scale factor for polar coordinates is $|r| = r$, meaning $dx\, dy = r\, dr\, d\theta$, and (7.1.5) becomes

$$\int_S f\left(x, y\right) dx\, dy = \int_D f\left(x\left(r, \theta\right), y\left(r, \theta\right)\right) r\, dr\, d\theta.$$

Schulz and Schulz [18] state:

> This [Equation (7.1.4)] is the famous change of variable formula. In most
> calculus books they do not prove it because the proof without differential
> forms is somewhat difficult. Using differential forms it is quite easy, as you
> have seen. The reason for this is that differential forms keep control of the
> orientation, whereas old techniques have to deal with it in an ad hoc and
> confusing way ... Everything we have done here in two dimensions will
> work perfectly well in n-dimensions.

Here is the oriented version of the formula for three dimensions:

$$\int_M f(x, y, z)\, dx \wedge dy \wedge dz =$$

$$\int_D f(x(u, v, w), y(u, v, w), z(u, v, w)) \det \left(\frac{\partial(x, y, z)}{\partial(u, v, w)} \right) du \wedge dv \wedge dw, \qquad (7.1.6)$$

where M is a region of xyz space, D is a region of uvw space and

$$\det \left(\frac{\partial(x, y, z)}{\partial(u, v, w)} \right) = \begin{vmatrix} \frac{\partial x}{\partial u} & \frac{\partial x}{\partial v} & \frac{\partial x}{\partial w} \\ \frac{\partial y}{\partial u} & \frac{\partial y}{\partial v} & \frac{\partial y}{\partial w} \\ \frac{\partial z}{\partial u} & \frac{\partial z}{\partial v} & \frac{\partial z}{\partial w} \end{vmatrix}.$$

7.1.1 The pullback

The change of variables formula we've just discussed is a special case of something
called the pullback. Hubbard and Hubbard [11] comment:

> The pullback describes how integrals transform under changes of variables.
> It ... underlies the change of variables formula for integrals ... Forms
> were largely invented to keep track of such changes of variables in multiple
> integrals, so the pullback plays a central role in the subject.

The pullback generalises the method of 'integration by substitution', where we can
solve integrals of the form

$$\int f(g(x)) g'(x)\, dx,$$

(where $g'(x)$ is the derivative of $g(x)$), by substituting $u = g(x)$. For example, to
solve

$$\int \cos(x^2)\, 2x\, dx,$$

we can say $f = \cos()$, $g(x) = x^2$ and $g'(x) = 2x$. We set $u = x^2$, $du = 2x\, dx$ and
write

$$\int f(g(x)) g'(x)\, dx = \int f(u)\, du$$

$$= \int \cos u \, du$$

$$= \sin u + C$$

$$= \sin \left(x^2 \right) + C,$$

where C is a constant of integration. And we have just computed a pullback. In short, when you see 'pullback', think 'change of variables'.

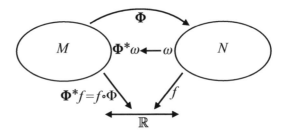

Figure 7.1: Pullback of function f and differential form ω from N to M.

With reference to differential forms, we need to consider pullbacks at a slightly more abstract level. Figure 7.1 shows two manifolds, M and N (which may or may not be of the same dimension and may or may not be subsets of some other manifold) and their associated pullbacks. Providing we have a smooth function Φ from M to N, we can transfer (or pull back) structures from N to structures on M. This is a roundabout way of saying we can change structures expressed in one set of variables on N into equivalent structures, using another set of variables, on M. In other words, the pullback is a change of variable formula.

The first thing we can pull back is a function (aka a 0-form) f that goes from N to $\mathbb{R}$. We can change this to a function from M to $\mathbb{R}$ by composing Φ with f and define (using a superscript asterisk)

$$\Phi^* f = f \circ \Phi,$$

where $\Phi^* f$ is called the pullback of f by Φ.

Example 7.1. From Edwards [8]. Manifolds M (with coordinates u, v) and N (with coordinates x, y) are both in $\mathbb{R}^2$. A function from M to N is $\Phi\left(u, v \right) = \left(2u - v, 3u + 2v \right)$, ie $x = 2u - v$ and $y = 3u + 2v$. If

$$f \left(x, y \right) = x^2 - y^2,$$

find $\Phi^* f$.

The pullback of f by Φ is given by

$$\Phi^* f \left(u, v \right) = f \circ \Phi$$

$$= (2u - v)^2 - (3u + 2v)^2$$
$$= -5u^2 - 16uv - 3v^2.$$

The second thing we can pull back is a differential form on N to a differential form on M. The pullback of a k-form ω on N is a k-form on M, denoted by (again using a superscript asterisk) $\mathbf{\Phi}^*\omega$. An example of how this works was outlined in the previous section when, using a change of variables from x, y to u, v, we expressed the 2-form

$$\omega = f(x, y)\ dx \wedge dy,$$

as

$$f(x(u, v), y(u, v)) \det\left(\frac{\partial(x, y)}{\partial(u, v)}\right) du \wedge dv.$$

Example 7.2. From Hubbard and Hubbard [11]. A manifold M (with coordinates u, v) is in $\mathbb{R}^2$. A manifold N (with coordinates x, y, z) is in $\mathbb{R}^3$. A function from M to N is $\mathbf{\Phi}(u, v) = \left(u^2, uv, v^2\right)$, ie $x = u^2, y = uv$ and $z = v^2$. If the 2-form

$$\omega = f(x, y, z)\ dx \wedge dz = y\, dx \wedge dz,$$

find $\mathbf{\Phi}^*\omega$.

The differential dx is

$$dx = \frac{\partial x}{\partial u} du + \frac{\partial x}{\partial v} dv,$$

which we can write as

$$d(u^2) = 2u\, du + 0\, dv = 2u\, du.$$

And the differential dz is

$$dz = \frac{\partial z}{\partial u} du + \frac{\partial z}{\partial v} dv,$$

which we can write as

$$d\left(v^2\right) = 0\, du + 2v\, dv = 2v\, dv.$$

The pullback of ω by $\mathbf{\Phi}$ is then given by

$$\mathbf{\Phi}^*\omega = f \circ \mathbf{\Phi}\, d\left(u^2\right) \wedge d\left(v^2\right)$$
$$= uv\,(2u\, du) \wedge (2v\, dv)$$
$$= 4u^2 v^2 du \wedge dv.$$

Important properties of the pullback are:

- If ω and ν are k-forms on N, then $\mathbf{\Phi}^*(\omega + \nu) = \mathbf{\Phi}^*\omega + \mathbf{\Phi}^*\nu$.

- If ω and ν are k-forms on N, then $\mathbf{\Phi}^*(\omega \wedge \nu) = \mathbf{\Phi}^*\omega \wedge \mathbf{\Phi}^*\nu$.

- If ω is a k-form on N, then the pullback of ω commutes with the exterior derivative, ie $\mathbf{\Phi}^*(d\omega) = d(\mathbf{\Phi}^*\omega)$.

7.2 Defining the integral

We can now meaningfully define the integral (7.0.1)

$$\int_M \omega.$$

We mentioned earlier that there are two definitions of this integral. One for when a differential k-form is integrated over a k-dimensional manifold in $\mathbb{R}^n$, where $k < n$. And a more straightforward one for when a differential n-form is integrated over an n-dimensional manifold in $\mathbb{R}^n$. Here they are.

7.2.1 k-form integrated over a k-dimensional manifold in $\mathbb{R}^n$, where $k < n$

Say we have a k-form integrated over a k-dimensional manifold M parameterised by

$$\Phi\left(u^1, \ldots, u^k\right)$$

in $\mathbb{R}^n$, where $k < n$. An example might be a 1-form integrated over a curve in $\mathbb{R}^3$, or a 3-form integrated over a three-dimensional manifold M in $\mathbb{R}^4$. Then by definition,

$$\int_M \omega = \pm \int_D \Phi^*\omega = \pm \int_D \omega\left(\frac{\partial\Phi}{\partial u^1}, \ldots, \frac{\partial\Phi}{\partial u^k}\right) du^1 \cdots du^n, \qquad (7.2.1)$$

where D is a region of $u^1, \ldots, u^k$ space. We know from the previous section that $\Phi^*\omega$ refers to the pullback of ω by Φ, which here describes how the integral transforms under a change of variables. If you find the pullback term distracting, feel free to ignore it and simplify (7.2.1) to

$$\int_M \omega = \pm \int_D \omega\left(\frac{\partial\Phi}{\partial u^1}, \ldots, \frac{\partial\Phi}{\partial u^k}\right) du^1 \cdots du^n.$$

Just remember that when you see a pullback, you'll also be seeing some sort of change of variables.

The integral of ω over M is plus or minus the right-hand integral depending on the parameterisation. Recall that a manifold that is orientable has one of two orientations. For a given orientation of M, some parameterisations will need a '+' sign and others a '−' sign in (7.2.1) in order to give the same answer. That sounds confusing – how do we know which sign to use? Fortunately, there's a neat way around this problem.

- When we parameterise a manifold M, that parameterisation will induce an orientation on M. As long as we make use of that induced orientation, we can use (7.2.1) with a '+' sign . Furthermore, if you're asked a question along the lines of 'Integrate a k-form over a k-dimensional manifold M parameterised by blah, blah, blah', where no orientation is specified, assume the desired orientation is the induced one and again use the '+' version of (7.2.1).

(Note that if you decide to make the integral easier by using a different way to parameterise M, you can't assume that the orientation induced by the new parameterisation will be the same as the orientation induced by the old parameterisation. There are ways of checking whether a new parameterisation preserves orientation, but we won't go there.)

So, assuming (as we do throughout this book) that we are using the orientation of M induced by the parameterisation, we can drop the '$-$' sign and write (7.2.1) as

$$\int_M \omega = \int_D \Phi^* \omega = \int_D \omega \left(\frac{\partial \Phi}{\partial u^1}, \dots, \frac{\partial \Phi}{\partial u^k} \right) du^1 \cdots du^n. \qquad (7.2.2)$$

This definition follows logically from the change of variables formula. For example, let's look at integrating a 2-form over a two-dimensional manifold S. Equation (7.2.2) then becomes

$$\int_S \omega = \int_D \Phi^* \omega = \int_D \omega \left(\frac{\partial \Phi}{\partial u}, \frac{\partial \Phi}{\partial v} \right) du \, dv, \qquad (7.2.3)$$

where S is a surface parameterised by $\Phi(u, v)$, ω is a 2-form and D is some region of the uv plane. Let's assume $\omega = dx \wedge dy$. Equation (2.3.5) tells us how ω acts on the tangent vectors $\frac{\partial \Phi}{\partial u}$ and $\frac{\partial \Phi}{\partial v}$:

$$(dx \wedge dy) \left(\frac{\partial \Phi}{\partial u}, \frac{\partial \Phi}{\partial v} \right) = \begin{vmatrix} \frac{\partial x}{\partial u} & \frac{\partial x}{\partial v} \\ \frac{\partial y}{\partial u} & \frac{\partial y}{\partial v} \end{vmatrix}. \qquad (7.2.4)$$

From the change of variables formula (7.1.1), we have

$$dx \wedge dy = \begin{vmatrix} \frac{\partial x}{\partial u} & \frac{\partial x}{\partial v} \\ \frac{\partial y}{\partial u} & \frac{\partial y}{\partial v} \end{vmatrix} du \wedge dv.$$

So we can say

$$dx \wedge dy = (dx \wedge dy) \left(\frac{\partial \Phi}{\partial u}, \frac{\partial \Phi}{\partial v} \right) du \wedge dv$$

$$\omega = \omega \left(\frac{\partial \Phi}{\partial u}, \frac{\partial \Phi}{\partial v} \right) du \wedge dv,$$

and hence the integral

$$\int_S \omega = \int_D \omega \left(\frac{\partial \Phi}{\partial u}, \frac{\partial \Phi}{\partial v} \right) du \, dv.$$

Similarly, for a 3-form integrated over a three-dimensional manifold M parameterised by $\Phi(u, v, w)$. Equation (7.2.2) then becomes

$$\int_M \omega = \int_D \Phi^* \omega = \int_D \omega \left(\frac{\partial \Phi}{\partial u}, \frac{\partial \Phi}{\partial v}, \frac{\partial \Phi}{\partial w} \right) du \, dv \, dw, \qquad (7.2.5)$$

where ω is a 3-form and D is some region of uvw space. As in section 2.4.3, we'll assume we're working in $\mathbb{R}^4$ (with coordinates x^1, x^2, x^3, x^4) with the 3-form $\omega = dx^1 \wedge dx^2 \wedge dx^4$. Equation (2.4.2) tells us how ω acts on the tangent vectors $\frac{\partial \Phi}{\partial u}$, $\frac{\partial \Phi}{\partial v}$ and $\frac{\partial \Phi}{\partial w}$:

$$\left(dx^1 \wedge dx^2 \wedge dx^4\right)\left(\frac{\partial \Phi}{\partial u}, \frac{\partial \Phi}{\partial v}, \frac{\partial \Phi}{\partial w}\right) = \begin{vmatrix} \frac{\partial x^1}{\partial u} & \frac{\partial x^1}{\partial v} & \frac{\partial x^1}{\partial w} \\ \frac{\partial x^2}{\partial u} & \frac{\partial x^2}{\partial v} & \frac{\partial x^2}{\partial w} \\ \frac{\partial x^4}{\partial u} & \frac{\partial x^4}{\partial v} & \frac{\partial x^4}{\partial w} \end{vmatrix}.$$

From the change of variables formula (7.1.6), we have

$$dx^1 \wedge dx^2 \wedge dx^4 = \begin{vmatrix} \frac{\partial x^1}{\partial u} & \frac{\partial x^1}{\partial v} & \frac{\partial x^1}{\partial w} \\ \frac{\partial x^2}{\partial u} & \frac{\partial x^2}{\partial v} & \frac{\partial x^2}{\partial w} \\ \frac{\partial x^4}{\partial u} & \frac{\partial x^4}{\partial v} & \frac{\partial x^4}{\partial w} \end{vmatrix} du \wedge dv \wedge dw.$$

So we can say

$$dx^1 \wedge dx^2 \wedge dx^4 = \left(dx^1 \wedge dx^2 \wedge dx^4\right)\left(\frac{\partial \Phi}{\partial u}, \frac{\partial \Phi}{\partial v}, \frac{\partial \Phi}{\partial w}\right) du \wedge dv \wedge dw$$

$$\omega = \omega\left(\frac{\partial \Phi}{\partial u}, \frac{\partial \Phi}{\partial v}, \frac{\partial \Phi}{\partial w}\right) du \wedge dv \wedge dw,$$

and hence the integral

$$\int_M \omega = \int_D \omega\left(\frac{\partial \Phi}{\partial u}, \frac{\partial \Phi}{\partial v}, \frac{\partial \Phi}{\partial w}\right) du\, dv\, dw.$$

And so on for higher dimensional differential forms.

7.2.2 n-form integrated over an n-dimensional manifold in $\mathbb{R}^n$

Now let's look at what happens in $\mathbb{R}^n$ when we integrate an n-form over an n-dimensional manifold M. (A top-dimensional form such as this is known as a volume form.) An example might be a 2-form integrated over a surface in $\mathbb{R}^2$, or a 3-form integrated over a region of $\mathbb{R}^3$. Then, for the n-form $\omega = f\left(x^1, \ldots, x^n\right) dx^1 \wedge dx^2 \cdots \wedge dx^n$,

$$\int_M \omega = \pm \int_M f\left(x^1, \ldots, x^n\right) dx^1 \cdots dx^n. \tag{7.2.6}$$

As in the previous section, we'll assume we are using the induced orientation of M and so we can write (7.2.6) with a '+' sign:

$$\int_M \omega = \int_M f\left(x^1, \ldots, x^n\right) dx^1 \cdots dx^n. \tag{7.2.7}$$

This definition also follows logically from the change of variables formula. For example, in $\mathbb{R}^2$ let's look at integrating a 2-form $\omega = f(x, y)\, dx \wedge dy$ over a (two-dimensional) surface S parameterised by $\mathbf{\Phi}(u, v)$ and where D is some region of the uv plane. Using (7.2.3) we can write

$$\int_S \omega = \int_D \mathbf{\Phi}^*\omega = \int_D \omega \left(\frac{\partial \mathbf{\Phi}}{\partial u}, \frac{\partial \mathbf{\Phi}}{\partial v} \right) du\, dv$$

$$= \int_D f(x(u, v), y(u, v)) (dx \wedge dy) \left(\frac{\partial \mathbf{\Phi}}{\partial u}, \frac{\partial \mathbf{\Phi}}{\partial v} \right) du\, dv$$

$$= \int_D f(x(u, v), y(u, v)) \left| \begin{matrix} \frac{\partial x}{\partial u} & \frac{\partial x}{\partial v} \\ \frac{\partial y}{\partial u} & \frac{\partial y}{\partial v} \end{matrix} \right| du\, dv. \tag{7.2.8}$$

But the change of variables formula (7.1.4) tells us that this is equal to

$$\pm \int_S f(x, y)\, dx\, dy,$$

where the $\pm$ sign appears because (7.2.8) did not use the *absolute* value of the determinant.

So we return to

$$\int_S \omega = \pm \int_S f(x, y)\, dx\, dy,$$

the two-dimensional version of (7.2.6).

There's also a one-dimension version of (7.2.7), which you are no doubt familiar with. This is the definite integral of single-variable calculus:

$$\int_b^a f(x)\, dx,$$

where the 1-form $f(x)\, dx$ is integrated over the oriented interval (aka a one-dimensional manifold) $[a, b]$.

We have seen that there are two definitions of the integral

$$\int_M \omega,$$

both dependent on the change of variables formula. Integration of differential forms and the change of variables formula are fundamental to each other.

As Fortney [9] remarks:

It turns out that differential forms are actually very nice things to integrate. Indeed, there is an intimate relationship between the integration of differential forms and the change-of-variables formulas you learned in calculus.

Or, as an anonymous online author [1] nicely puts it:

> The whole point of differential forms is that integration of forms is designed to work consistently with the change of variables formula. Or another way to think of it, is that the change of variables formula is baked into the definition of differential forms.

7.2.3 The recipe

A few examples should make things clearer. First, here's a recap of the rules for integrating differential forms.

1. A differential k-form ω must be integrated over an oriented k-dimensional manifold M.

2. If necessary, choose a convenient parameterisation $\mathbf{\Phi}\left(u^1, \ldots, u^k\right)$ of M. Use the orientation of M induced by this parameterisation.

3. For an n-dimensional space where $k < n$ use (7.2.2):

$$\int_M \omega = \int_D \mathbf{\Phi}^* \omega = \int_D \omega\left(\frac{\partial \mathbf{\Phi}}{\partial u^1}, \ldots, \frac{\partial \mathbf{\Phi}}{\partial u^k}\right) du^1 \cdots du^n.$$

4. And for an n-dimensional space where $k = n$ (ie for a volume form) use (7.2.7):

$$\int_M \omega = \int_M f\left(x^1, \ldots, x^n\right) dx^1 \cdots dx^n.$$

7.2.4 Some examples

Example 7.3. From Bryan [7]. Integrate the 1-form $\omega = 2y\, dx - xz\, dy + dz$ over a curve C, where C is parameterised by $\mathbf{\Phi}(t) = \left(3t, t^2, 5 - t\right)$ for $0 \le t \le 2$.

Here M is the curve C, and (7.2.2) becomes

$$\int_C \omega = \int_{[0,2]} \mathbf{\Phi}^* \omega = \int_0^2 \omega\left(\frac{d\mathbf{\Phi}}{dt}\right) dt.$$

The tangent vector $\frac{d\mathbf{\Phi}}{dt}$ along C is given by

$$\frac{d\mathbf{\Phi}}{dt} = \left(\frac{dx}{dt}, \frac{dy}{dt}, \frac{dz}{dt}\right)$$

86

$$= (3, 2t, -1).$$

$$\int_C \omega = \int_0^2 \omega \left(\frac{d\Phi}{dt} \right) dt$$

$$= \int_0^2 \omega \left(3, 2t, -1 \right) dt$$

$$= \int_0^2 \left((2y \times 3) - (xz \times 2t) + (-1) \right) dt$$

$$= \int_0^2 \left(6t^2 - \left(30t^2 - 6t^3 \right) - 1 \right) dt$$

$$\int_0^2 \left(6t^3 - 24t^2 - 1 \right) dt$$

$$= \left. \left(\frac{3t^4}{2} - 8t^3 - t \right) \right|_0^2$$

$$= -42.$$

Example 7.4. From Bryan [7]. In $\mathbb{R}^4$, with coordinates x^1, x^2, x^3, x^4, integrate the 2-form $\omega = x^2 dx^1 \wedge dx^3 - x^4 dx^3 \wedge dx^4$ over a surface S, where S is parameterised by $\Phi(u, v) = (u, u - v, 3 - u + uv, -3v)$ for $u^2 + v^2 \le 1$.

Here M is the surface S, and (7.2.2) becomes (7.2.3)

$$\int_S \omega = \int_D \Phi^* \omega = \int_D \omega \left(\frac{\partial \Phi}{\partial u}, \frac{\partial \Phi}{\partial v} \right) du\, dv.$$

The tangent vectors to S are

$$\frac{\partial \Phi}{\partial u} = \left(\frac{\partial x^1}{\partial u}, \frac{\partial x^2}{\partial u}, \frac{\partial x^3}{\partial u}, \frac{\partial x^4}{\partial u} \right)$$

$$= (1, 1, v - 1, 0)$$

and

$$\frac{\partial \Phi}{\partial v} = \left(\frac{\partial x^1}{\partial v}, \frac{\partial x^2}{\partial v}, \frac{\partial x^3}{\partial v}, \frac{\partial x^4}{\partial v} \right)$$

$$= (0, -1, u, -3).$$

A version of (7.2.4) tells us that the 2-form $dx^1 \wedge dx^3$ acts on tangents vectors $\frac{\partial \Phi}{\partial u}$ and $\frac{\partial \Phi}{\partial v}$ as

$$\left(dx^1 \wedge dx^3 \right) \left(\frac{\partial \Phi}{\partial u}, \frac{\partial \Phi}{\partial v} \right) = \begin{vmatrix} \frac{\partial x^1}{\partial u} & \frac{\partial x^1}{\partial v} \\ \frac{\partial x^3}{\partial u} & \frac{\partial x^3}{\partial v} \end{vmatrix}.$$

And the 2-form $dx^3 \wedge dx^4$ acts on tangents vectors $\frac{\partial \Phi}{\partial u}$ and $\frac{\partial \Phi}{\partial v}$ as

$$\left(dx^3 \wedge dx^4\right) \left(\frac{\partial \Phi}{\partial u}, \frac{\partial \Phi}{\partial v}\right) = \begin{vmatrix} \frac{\partial x^3}{\partial u} & \frac{\partial x^3}{\partial v} \\ \frac{\partial x^4}{\partial u} & \frac{\partial x^4}{\partial v} \end{vmatrix}.$$

Plug these into

$$\int_S \omega = \int_D \omega \left(\frac{\partial \Phi}{\partial u}, \frac{\partial \Phi}{\partial v}\right) du\, dv$$

and we get

$$\int_S \omega = \int_D \left(x^2 \begin{vmatrix} \frac{\partial x^1}{\partial u} & \frac{\partial x^1}{\partial v} \\ \frac{\partial x^3}{\partial u} & \frac{\partial x^3}{\partial v} \end{vmatrix} - x^4 \begin{vmatrix} \frac{\partial x^3}{\partial u} & \frac{\partial x^3}{\partial v} \\ \frac{\partial x^4}{\partial u} & \frac{\partial x^4}{\partial v} \end{vmatrix}\right) du\, dv$$

$$= \int_D \left(x^2 \begin{vmatrix} 1 & 0 \\ v-1 & u \end{vmatrix} - x^4 \begin{vmatrix} v-1 & u \\ 0 & -3 \end{vmatrix}\right) du\, dv$$

$$= \int_D \left(x^2 u - x^4 (3 - 3v)\right) du\, dv$$

$$= \int_D \left((u - v) u + 3v (3 - 3v)\right) du\, dv$$

$$= \int_D \left(u^2 - uv + 9v - 9v^2\right) du\, dv.$$

You might recognise the parameterisation $u^2 + v^2 \leq 1$ as representing the unit disk in the uv plane. So we can say

$$\int_S \omega = \int_D \left(u^2 - uv + 9v - 9v^2\right) du\, dv = \int_{-1}^{1} \int_{-\sqrt{1-v^2}}^{\sqrt{1-v^2}} \left(u^2 - uv + 9v - 9v^2\right) du\, dv$$

$$\int_S \omega = -2\pi.$$

You can check this result using the WolframAlpha online calculator [22] by typing the following into the input box and hitting Enter:

```
integrate (integrate (u^2 - uv + 9v - 9v^2) du from u = -((1 -
v^2)^(1/2)) to ((1 - v^2)^(1/2))) dv from v = -1 to 1
```

Alternatively, we can note the circular symmetry of the unit disk and convert the integral to polar coordinates using $u = r \cos \theta$, $v = r \sin \theta$ and $du\, dv = r\, dr\, d\theta$ to give

$$\int_S \omega = \int_0^{2\pi} \int_0^1 \left(r^2 \cos^2 \theta - r^2 \cos \theta \sin \theta + 9r \sin \theta - 9r^2 \sin^2 \theta\right) r\, dr\, d\theta,$$

with nice constant limits. Also, the second and third terms are odd functions (ie total positive area cancels total negative area) in θ, which integrated on $[0, 2\pi]$ give zero, so we have

$$\int_S \omega = \int_0^{2\pi} \int_0^1 \left(r^2 \cos^2 \theta - 9r^2 \sin^2 \theta\right) r \, dr \, d\theta$$

$$= -2\pi.$$

You can check this result using the WolframAlpha online calculator [22] by typing the following into the input box and hitting Enter:

```
integrate (integrate ((r^2)*((cos theta)^2) - 9*(r^2)(sin theta)^2)r
dr from r = 0 to 1)dtheta from theta = 0 to 2*Pi
```

Example 7.5. From Schulz and Schulz [18]. In $\mathbb{R}^2$, integrate the 2-form $\omega = x \, dy \wedge dx$ over a surface S, where S is a unit disk.

We are integrating a 2-form over a surface in $\mathbb{R}^2$. ω is therefore a volume form, so we can use a variant of (7.2.7):

$$\int_S \omega = \int_S f(x, y) \, dx \, dy.$$

This is similar, though more straightforward, than the previous example, where we were also integrating over the unit disk. Notice that the differentials dx and dy are not in the correct order. We fix this by saying

$$\int_S \omega = \int_S x \, dy \wedge dx = - \int_S x \, dx \wedge dy,$$

which we can then write as the ordinary (ie unoriented) double integral

$$- \int_S x \, dx \, dy.$$

As we're integrating x over the unit disk we *could* say

$$- \int_S x \, dx \, dy = - \int_{-1}^1 \int_{-\sqrt{1-x^2}}^{\sqrt{1-x^2}} x \, dx \, dy.$$

But, as with the previous example, this is easier if we convert the integral to polar coordinates using $x = r \cos \theta$ and $dx \, dy = r \, dr \, d\theta$ to give

$$- \int_S x \, dx \, dy = - \int_0^{2\pi} \int_0^1 (r \cos \theta) r \, dr \, d\theta$$

$$= 0.$$

You can check this result using the WolframAlpha online calculator [22] by typing the following into the input box and hitting Enter:

```
- integrate (integrate (r*cos(theta))r dr from r = 0 to 1)dtheta from
theta = 0 to 2*Pi
```

Example 7.6. From Bryan [7]. In $\mathbb{R}^4$, with coordinates x^1, x^2, x^3, x^4, integrate the 3-form $\omega = x^3 dx^1 \wedge dx^2 \wedge dx^4$ over a three-dimensional manifold M, where M is parameterised by $\Phi(u, v, w) = (vw, u^2, 1 - 3v + w, uv)$ for $u^2 + v^2 + w^2 \leq 1$.

Equation (7.2.2) becomes (7.2.5)

$$\int_M \omega = \int_D \Phi^* \omega = \int_D \omega \left(\frac{\partial \Phi}{\partial u}, \frac{\partial \Phi}{\partial v}, \frac{\partial \Phi}{\partial w} \right) du\, dv\, dw.$$

The tangent vectors to M are

$$\frac{\partial \Phi}{\partial u} = \left(\frac{\partial x^1}{\partial u}, \frac{\partial x^2}{\partial u}, \frac{\partial x^3}{\partial u}, \frac{\partial x^4}{\partial u} \right)$$

$$= (0, 2u, 0, v)$$

and

$$\frac{\partial \Phi}{\partial v} = \left(\frac{\partial x^1}{\partial v}, \frac{\partial x^2}{\partial v}, \frac{\partial x^3}{\partial v}, \frac{\partial x^4}{\partial v} \right)$$

$$= (w, 0, -3, u)$$

and

$$\frac{\partial \Phi}{\partial w} = \left(\frac{\partial x^1}{\partial w}, \frac{\partial x^2}{\partial w}, \frac{\partial x^3}{\partial w}, \frac{\partial x^4}{\partial w} \right)$$

$$= (v, 0, 1, 0) .$$

Equation (2.4.2)

$$\left(dx^1 \wedge dx^2 \wedge dx^4 \right) \left(\frac{\partial \Phi}{\partial u}, \frac{\partial \Phi}{\partial v}, \frac{\partial \Phi}{\partial w} \right) = \begin{vmatrix} \frac{\partial x^1}{\partial u} & \frac{\partial x^1}{\partial v} & \frac{\partial x^1}{\partial w} \\ \frac{\partial x^2}{\partial u} & \frac{\partial x^2}{\partial v} & \frac{\partial x^2}{\partial w} \\ \frac{\partial x^4}{\partial u} & \frac{\partial x^4}{\partial v} & \frac{\partial x^4}{\partial w} \end{vmatrix}$$

tells us how the 3-form $dx^1 \wedge dx^2 \wedge dx^4$ acts on tangents vectors $\frac{\partial \Phi}{\partial u}$, $\frac{\partial \Phi}{\partial v}$ and $\frac{\partial \Phi}{\partial w}$.

Plug this into

$$\int_M \omega = \int_D \omega \left(\frac{\partial \Phi}{\partial u}, \frac{\partial \Phi}{\partial v}, \frac{\partial \Phi}{\partial w} \right) du\, dv\, dw$$

and we get

$$\int_M \omega = \int_D x^3 \begin{vmatrix} \dfrac{\partial x^1}{\partial u} & \dfrac{\partial x^1}{\partial v} & \dfrac{\partial x^1}{\partial w} \\ \dfrac{\partial x^2}{\partial u} & \dfrac{\partial x^2}{\partial v} & \dfrac{\partial x^2}{\partial w} \\ \dfrac{\partial x^4}{\partial u} & \dfrac{\partial x^4}{\partial v} & \dfrac{\partial x^4}{\partial w} \end{vmatrix} du\, dv\, dw$$

$$= \int_D x^3 \begin{vmatrix} 0 & w & v \\ 2u & 0 & 0 \\ v & u & 0 \end{vmatrix} du\, dv\, dw$$

$$\int_M \omega = \int_D \left(2u^2 v - 6u^2 v^2 + 2u^2 vw \right) du\, dv\, dw.$$

You might recognise the parameterisation $u^2 + v^2 + w^2 \leq 1$ as representing the unit ball in uvw space. So we *could* say

$$\int_M \omega = \int_{-1}^{1} \int_{-\sqrt{1-w^2}}^{\sqrt{1-w^2}} \int_{-\sqrt{1-w^2-v^2}}^{\sqrt{1-w^2-v^2}} \left(2u^2 v - 6u^2 v^2 + 2u^2 vw \right) du\, dv\, dw,$$

and good luck with that. A better option is to note the spherical symmetry of a ball and convert to spherical coordinates using $u = r \sin \phi \cos \theta$, $v = r \sin \phi \sin \theta$, $w = r \cos \phi$ and $du\, dv\, dw = r^2 \sin \phi\, dr\, d\theta\, d\phi$. This gives

$$\int_M \omega = \int_0^\pi \int_0^{2\pi} \int_0^1 \left(\left(2r^5 \sin^4 \phi \cos^2 \theta \sin \theta \right) - \left(6r^6 \sin^5 \phi \cos^2 \theta \sin^2 \theta \right) \right.$$

$$\left. + \left(2r^6 \sin^4 \phi \cos^2 \theta \sin \theta \cos \phi \right) \right) dr\, d\theta\, d\phi,$$

which has nice constant limits. Also, the first and last terms are odd functions in θ, which integrated on $[0, 2\pi]$ give zero. So we now have

$$\int_M \omega = \int_0^\pi \int_0^{2\pi} \int_0^1 \left(-6r^6 \sin^5 \phi \cos^2 \theta \sin^2 \theta \right) dr\, d\theta\, d\phi$$

$$\int_M \omega = -\frac{8\pi}{35}.$$

You can check this result using the WolframAlpha online calculator [22] by typing the following into the input box and hitting Enter:

```
integrate (integrate (integrate -(6r^6)*((sin phi)^5)*((cos
theta)^2)*((sin theta)^2) dr from r = 0 to 1) dtheta from theta =
0 to 2*Pi) dphi from phi = 0 to Pi
```

7.3 Independence of parameterisation

We mentioned at the start of this chapter that the integral (7.0.1)

$$\int_M \omega$$

does not depend on how M is parameterised. We'll now show this for parameterised curves and surfaces in $\mathbb{R}^3$. The argument can, of course, be extended to other spaces of arbitrary dimension.

7.3.1 Parameterised curves

If we want to integrate a 1-form ω over a curve C, where C is parameterised by $\boldsymbol{\Phi}(t)$ for $a \leq t \leq b$, (7.2.2) becomes

$$\int_C \omega = \int_a^b \omega\left(\frac{d\boldsymbol{\Phi}}{dt}\right) dt \qquad (7.3.1)$$

$$= \int_a^b \omega\left(\frac{dx}{dt}, \frac{dy}{dt}, \frac{dz}{dt}\right) dt.$$

Now we change the parameterisation to $\boldsymbol{\Phi}(s)$ for $c \leq s \leq d$, where $s = c$ if and only if $t = a$, and $s = d$ if and only if $t = b$. We need to show that

$$\int_a^b \omega\left(\frac{d\boldsymbol{\Phi}}{dt}\right) dt = \int_c^d \omega\left(\frac{d\boldsymbol{\Phi}}{ds}\right) ds$$

$$\int_a^b \omega\left(\frac{dx}{dt}, \frac{dy}{dt}, \frac{dz}{dt}\right) dt = \int_c^d \omega\left(\frac{dx}{ds}, \frac{dy}{ds}, \frac{dz}{ds}\right) ds.$$

First, use the chain rule

$$\frac{d\boldsymbol{\Phi}}{dt} = \frac{d\boldsymbol{\Phi}}{ds}\frac{ds}{dt},$$

and substitute into (7.3.1) to give

$$\int_a^b \omega\left(\frac{d\boldsymbol{\Phi}}{dt}\right) dt = \int_a^b \omega\left(\frac{d\boldsymbol{\Phi}}{ds}\frac{ds}{dt}\right) dt.$$

We can change the differential dt to ds by using

$$ds = \frac{ds}{dt}dt,$$

and then write

$$\int_a^b \omega\left(\frac{d\boldsymbol{\Phi}}{dt}\right) dt = \int_c^d \omega\left(\frac{d\boldsymbol{\Phi}}{ds}\right) ds,$$

which is what we set out to show.

7.3.2 Parameterised surfaces

The change of variables formula (7.1.3)

$$\int_S f\, dx \wedge dy = \int_D f\, \det\left(\frac{\partial\,(x,y)}{\partial\,(u,v)}\right) du\, dv$$

describes a 2-form $\omega = f\, dx \wedge dy$ integrated over a surface S parameterised by u and v. If we parameterise the surface S using two different parameters, s and t for example, we get

$$\int_S f\, dx \wedge dy = \int_E f\, \det\left(\frac{\partial\,(x,y)}{\partial\,(s,t)}\right) ds\, dt,$$

where E is some region of the st plane. To show independence of parameterisation we need to show that

$$\int_D f\, \det\left(\frac{\partial\,(x,y)}{\partial\,(u,v)}\right) du\, dv = \int_E f\, \det\left(\frac{\partial\,(x,y)}{\partial\,(s,t)}\right) ds\, dt.$$

We first state a version of the chain rule in matrix form:

$$\begin{bmatrix} \frac{\partial x}{\partial s} & \frac{\partial x}{\partial t} \\ \frac{\partial y}{\partial s} & \frac{\partial y}{\partial t} \end{bmatrix} = \begin{bmatrix} \frac{\partial x}{\partial u} & \frac{\partial x}{\partial v} \\ \frac{\partial y}{\partial u} & \frac{\partial y}{\partial v} \end{bmatrix} \begin{bmatrix} \frac{\partial u}{\partial s} & \frac{\partial u}{\partial t} \\ \frac{\partial v}{\partial s} & \frac{\partial v}{\partial t} \end{bmatrix}.$$

Next, take the determinant of both sides, to give

$$\det\left(\frac{\partial\,(x,y)}{\partial\,(s,t)}\right) = \det\left(\frac{\partial\,(x,y)}{\partial\,(u,v)}\right) \det\left(\frac{\partial\,(u,v)}{\partial\,(s,t)}\right). \tag{7.3.2}$$

We can rewrite the change of variables formula (7.1.4)

$$\int_S f\, dx\, dy = \int_D f\, \left|\det\left(\frac{\partial\,(x,y)}{\partial\,(u,v)}\right)\right| du\, dv$$

in terms of our u,v and s,t parameterisations as

$$\int_D f\, \det\left(\frac{\partial\,(x,y)}{\partial\,(u,v)}\right) du\, dv = \int_E f\, \det\left(\frac{\partial\,(x,y)}{\partial\,(u,v)}\right) \left|\det\left(\frac{\partial\,(u,v)}{\partial\,(s,t)}\right)\right| ds\, dt. \tag{7.3.3}$$

If we assume that both parameterisations have the same orientation by requiring that $\det\left(\frac{\partial(u,v)}{\partial(s,t)}\right) > 0$, we can then drop the absolute sign on the right-hand side. If we substitute (7.3.2) into (7.3.3), we obtain

$$\int_D f\, \det\left(\frac{\partial\,(x,y)}{\partial\,(u,v)}\right) du\, dv = \int_E f\, \det\left(\frac{\partial\,(x,y)}{\partial\,(s,t)}\right) ds\, dt,$$

which is what we set out to show.

8 Integrating differential forms and vector calculus

In the previous chapter, we looked at how to integrate differential k-forms over k-dimensional manifolds in $\mathbb{R}^n$, where $k \leq n$. We'll now confine ourselves to $\mathbb{R}^2$ and $\mathbb{R}^3$ and relate what we have learned to the line, surface and volume integrals of vector calculus. These integrals are the building blocks of the big four integral theorems of vector calculus: the gradient theorem, Green's theorem, Stokes' theorem and the divergence theorem. As we'll see in chapter 9, these four theorems are themselves special cases of the generalised Stokes' theorem, which applies to spaces of arbitrary dimension.

The integrals discussed in this chapter can generally be understood *either* in terms of vector calculus or differential forms. Say we want to use a line integral to find the work done by a force field on a particle that moves along a curve. Using vector calculus, we'd assume force is a vector field; using differential forms, we'd assume force is a 1-form (the force 1-form or work form we met in section 2.2.7). Similarly, if we want to use a surface integral to find the flow of a fluid through a surface per unit time. We can do it the vector calculus way – representing the fluid as a vector field – or take the differential form route and use the 2-form (the flux form we met in section 2.3.3) associated with that vector field.

Some physical quantities, however, are more naturally described as differential forms rather than vectors. Two examples, that we'll meet when we look at Maxwell's equations in spacetime, are the electric field $\mathbf{E}$ and the magnetic field $\mathbf{B}$, which are more properly understood not as vector fields but as, respectively, a 1-form E and a 2-form B.

Line and surface integrals in vector calculus involve a dot product, which converts the vector field into a differential form. Integrating differential forms is therefore a more fundamental operation than integrating vector fields, as remarked upon by Frankel [10]:

> Exterior differential forms ... are the natural objects appearing as integrands of line, surface, and volume integrals as well as the n-dimensional generalizations required in, for example, Hamiltonian mechanics, relativity, and string theories. We shall see ... that one does not integrate vectors; one integrates forms. If there is extra structure available, for example, a Riemannian metric [a type of metric tensor], then it is possible to rephrase an integration, say of exterior 1-forms or 2-forms, in terms of a vector integrations involving 'arc lengths' or 'surface areas', but we shall see that

even in this case we are complicating a basically simple situation. If a line integral of a vector occurs in a problem, then usually a deeper look at the situation will show that the vector in question was in fact a covector; that is, a 1-form!

Or, as Arapura [2] states:

The calculus of differential forms give an alternative to vector calculus which is ultimately simpler and more flexible.

8.1 Line integrals

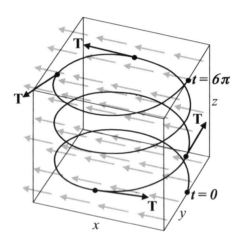

Figure 8.1: Line integral of a vector field.

An integral that is evaluated along a curve is called a line integral, such as in Example 7.3 where we integrated the 1-form $\omega = 2y\,dx - xz\,dy + dz$ over a curve parameterised by $\mathbf{\Phi}\left(t\right) = \left(3t, t^2, 5 - t\right)$ for $0 \leq t \leq 2$.

Figure 8.1 shows the curve C of

$$\mathbf{\Phi}\left(t\right) = \cos t\,\hat{\mathbf{e}}_x + \sin t\,\hat{\mathbf{e}}_y + \frac{t}{3\pi}\hat{\mathbf{e}}_z$$

for $0 \leq t \leq 6\pi$. At any point on C there are tangent vectors

$$\frac{d\mathbf{\Phi}}{dt}.$$

We require unit tangent vectors $\mathbf{T}$, found by dividing

$$\frac{d\mathbf{\Phi}}{dt}$$

by its magnitude, ie

$$\mathbf{T} = \frac{\frac{d\mathbf{\Phi}}{dt}}{\left\| \frac{d\mathbf{\Phi}}{dt} \right\|}. \tag{8.1.1}$$

Also shown (as grey arrows) is a vector field $\mathbf{v}(x, y, z)$. Let's assume that $\mathbf{v}$ represents a force field (a gravitational or magnetic field, for example) and that we move a particle along C from $t = 0$ to $t = 6\pi$. We can then interpret the line integral as the work done by the force field on the particle as it moves along C. At any point $\mathbf{\Phi}(t)$ on C, the component of $\mathbf{v}$ in the direction we're moving the particle is given by the dot product of $\mathbf{v}$ and $\mathbf{T}$, ie $\mathbf{v} \cdot \mathbf{T}$. If $\mathbf{v} \cdot \mathbf{T}$ is positive, the force field $\mathbf{v}$ is pushing with the particle moving along the curve. If $\mathbf{v} \cdot \mathbf{T}$ is negative, the force field is pushing against the particle's direction of travel.

Work equals force times distance, so if we multiply $\mathbf{v} \cdot \mathbf{T}$ by an infinitesimal displacement ds along C and then integrate that quantity we'll get the total work done by the force field $\mathbf{v}$ on the particle as we move it along C, ie the line integral:

$$\text{Work} = \int_C \mathbf{v} \cdot \mathbf{T} ds.$$

We want to express this equation in terms of the parameter t for the general limits $a \le t \le b$. We therefore use the definition of the unit tangent vector (8.1.1) and write

$$\int_C \mathbf{v} \cdot \mathbf{T} ds = \int_C \mathbf{v}(\mathbf{\Phi}(t)) \cdot \frac{\frac{d\mathbf{\Phi}}{dt}}{\left\| \frac{d\mathbf{\Phi}}{dt} \right\|} ds.$$

If we think of $\left\| \frac{d\mathbf{\Phi}}{dt} \right\|$ as a speed, we can say the distance ds travelled along C equals $\left\| \frac{d\mathbf{\Phi}}{dt} \right\|$ multiplied by time dt, to give

$$\int_C \mathbf{v} \cdot \mathbf{T} ds = \int_a^b \mathbf{v}(\mathbf{\Phi}(t)) \cdot \frac{\frac{d\mathbf{\Phi}}{dt}}{\left\| \frac{d\mathbf{\Phi}}{dt} \right\|} \left\| \frac{d\mathbf{\Phi}}{dt} \right\| dt$$

$$= \int_a^b \mathbf{v}(\mathbf{\Phi}(t)) \cdot \frac{d\mathbf{\Phi}}{dt} dt,$$

which is often written simply as

$$\int_C \mathbf{v} \cdot \mathbf{T} ds = \int_C \mathbf{v} \cdot d\mathbf{\Phi},$$

where

$$\int_C \mathbf{v} \cdot d\mathbf{\Phi} = \int_a^b \mathbf{v}(\mathbf{\Phi}(t)) \cdot \frac{d\mathbf{\Phi}}{dt} dt. \tag{8.1.2}$$

Example 8.1. From Paul's Online Notes [16]. Integrate the vector field $\mathbf{v}(x, y, z) = 8x^2yz\hat{\mathbf{e}}_x + 5z\hat{\mathbf{e}}_y - 4xy\hat{\mathbf{e}}_z$ over a curve C, where C is parameterised by $\mathbf{\Phi}(t) = t\hat{\mathbf{e}}_x + t^2\hat{\mathbf{e}}_y + t^3\hat{\mathbf{e}}_z$ for $0 \leq t \leq 1$.

We first need to express the vector field $\mathbf{v}$ in terms of t:

$$\mathbf{v}(\mathbf{\Phi}(t)) = 8t^2(t^2)(t^3)\hat{\mathbf{e}}_x + 5t^3\hat{\mathbf{e}}_y - 4t(t^2)\hat{\mathbf{e}}_z$$

$$= 8t^7\hat{\mathbf{e}}_x + 5t^3\hat{\mathbf{e}}_y - 4t^3\hat{\mathbf{e}}_z.$$

Then we find

$$\frac{d\mathbf{\Phi}}{dt} = \hat{\mathbf{e}}_x + 2t\hat{\mathbf{e}}_y + 3t^2\hat{\mathbf{e}}_z.$$

Using (8.1.2)

$$\int_C \mathbf{v} \cdot d\mathbf{\Phi} = \int_a^b \mathbf{v}(\mathbf{\Phi}(t)) \cdot \frac{d\mathbf{\Phi}}{dt} dt,$$

we dot these together to give

$$\int_C \mathbf{v} \cdot d\mathbf{\Phi} = \int_0^1 \left(8t^7\hat{\mathbf{e}}_x + 5t^3\hat{\mathbf{e}}_y - 4t^3\hat{\mathbf{e}}_z\right) \cdot \left(\hat{\mathbf{e}}_x + 2t\hat{\mathbf{e}}_y + 3t^2\hat{\mathbf{e}}_z\right) dt$$

$$= \int_0^1 \left(8t^7 + 10t^4 - 12t^5\right) dt$$

$$= \left(t^8 + 2t^5 - 2t^6\right)\big|_0^1$$

$$= 1.$$

8.1.1 Conservative vector fields

A conservative vector field is the gradient of a function. So if $\mathbf{v}$ is a vector field and $f(x, y, z)$ is the function, then

$$\mathbf{v} = \nabla f$$

is a conservative vector field.

For example, if we use (5.1.1)

$$\nabla f = \frac{\partial f}{\partial x}\hat{\mathbf{e}}_x + \frac{\partial f}{\partial y}\hat{\mathbf{e}}_y + \frac{\partial f}{\partial z}\hat{\mathbf{e}}_z$$

to find the gradient of the function

$$f(x, y, z) = xy^2z^3$$

we get the conservative vector field

$$y^2z^3\hat{\mathbf{e}}_x + 2xyz^3\hat{\mathbf{e}}_y + 3xy^2z^2\hat{\mathbf{e}}_z.$$

The function f is called the potential function of $\mathbf{v}$.

Importantly, line integrals of conservative vector fields are path independent (and consequently line integrals over a closed path are zero). The Earth's gravitational field is an example of a conservative vector field. If you lift a book off the floor and put it on a table, the work done by you against the gravitational field doesn't depend on the path the book takes. So you could pick up the book and put it directly on the table. Or you could pick up the book, take it on holiday with you and then put it on the table. In both cases, the total work you performed against the gravitational field would be the same.

The property of path independence means that in order to evaluate a line integral of a conservative vector field we only need to know the endpoints of our curve C. So if f is our potential function, ∇f is our conservative vector field $\mathbf{v}$ and C is parameterised by $\boldsymbol{\Phi}(t)$ for $a \leq t \leq b$, then

$$\int_C \mathbf{v} \cdot d\boldsymbol{\Phi} = \int_C \nabla f \cdot d\boldsymbol{\Phi} = f(\boldsymbol{\Phi}(b)) - f(\boldsymbol{\Phi}(a)). \qquad (8.1.3)$$

This is known as the gradient theorem or the fundamental theorem of calculus for line integrals.

8.1.2 And with differential forms ...

We start with the 1-form $\omega_1 = f_1\, dx + f_2\, dy + f_3\, dz$ that we know is associated with the vector field $\mathbf{v}(x, y, z) = f_1\hat{\mathbf{e}}_x + f_2\hat{\mathbf{e}}_y + f_3\hat{\mathbf{e}}_z$. A version of (7.2.2) tells us that the integral of ω_1 over a curve C parameterised by $\boldsymbol{\Phi}(t)$ for $a \leq t \leq b$ is given by

$$\int_C \omega_1 = \int_a^b \omega_1\left(\frac{d\boldsymbol{\Phi}}{dt}\right) dt$$

$$= \int_a^b (f_1\, dx + f_2\, dy + f_3\, dz)\left(\frac{dx}{dt}\hat{\mathbf{e}}_x, \frac{dy}{dt}\hat{\mathbf{e}}_y, \frac{dz}{dt}\hat{\mathbf{e}}_z\right) dt.$$

The basis 1-forms dx, dy, dz and basis vectors $\hat{\mathbf{e}}_x, \hat{\mathbf{e}}_y, \hat{\mathbf{e}}_z$ are dual to each other (2.2.4) and therefore disappear in a puff of zeros and ones, and we get

$$= \int_a^b \left(f_1\frac{dx}{dt} + f_2\frac{dy}{dt} + f_3\frac{dz}{dt}\right) dt,$$

which is equivalent to the vector calculus formula for the line integral (8.1.2), and therefore we have shown that

$$\int_C \omega_1 = \int_a^b \mathbf{v}(\boldsymbol{\Phi}(t)) \cdot \frac{d\boldsymbol{\Phi}}{dt}\, dt = \int_C \mathbf{v} \cdot d\boldsymbol{\Phi}.$$

99

And we can also conclude that

$$\int_C \mathbf{v} \cdot d\mathbf{\Phi} = \int_C f_1 \, dx + f_2 \, dy + f_3 \, dz. \tag{8.1.4}$$

We saw in section 5.1 that the gradient vector field ∇f can be associated with df, the exterior derivative of the 0-form $f(x, y, z)$. So for conservative vector fields

$$\int_C \nabla f \cdot d\mathbf{\Phi} = \int_C df.$$

8.2 Surface integrals

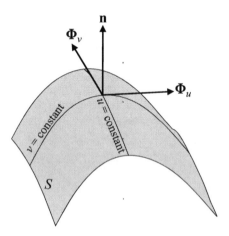

Figure 8.2: Tangent vectors $\mathbf{\Phi}_u$, $\mathbf{\Phi}_v$ and unit normal $\mathbf{n}$ on surface S.

An integral that is evaluated over a surface is called a surface integral.

A surface can be parameterised by two parameters. We'll use u and v as our two parameters and plug them into a vector $\mathbf{\Phi}(u, v)$ to define a surface S. In other words, S has the vector equation

$$\mathbf{\Phi}(u, v) = x(u, v)\,\hat{\mathbf{e}}_x + y(u, v)\,\hat{\mathbf{e}}_y + z(u, v)\,\hat{\mathbf{e}}_z.$$

At any point on S there are tangent vectors $\mathbf{\Phi}_u$ and $\mathbf{\Phi}_v$ (see Figure 8.2) given by

$$\mathbf{\Phi}_u = \frac{\partial x}{\partial u}\hat{\mathbf{e}}_x + \frac{\partial y}{\partial u}\hat{\mathbf{e}}_y + \frac{\partial z}{\partial u}\hat{\mathbf{e}}_z$$

and

$$\mathbf{\Phi}_v = \frac{\partial x}{\partial v}\hat{\mathbf{e}}_x + \frac{\partial y}{\partial v}\hat{\mathbf{e}}_y + \frac{\partial z}{\partial v}\hat{\mathbf{e}}_z.$$

We also require a unit normal vector field $\mathbf{n}$ of unit vectors perpendicular to S.

We can find $\mathbf{n}$ by first noting that a vector $\mathbf{x}$ perpendicular to S is given by the cross product of $\mathbf{\Phi}_u$ and $\mathbf{\Phi}_v$:

$$\mathbf{x} = \mathbf{\Phi}_u \times \mathbf{\Phi}_v.$$

The unit normal $\mathbf{n}$ is then found by dividing $\mathbf{x}$ by its magnitude, ie

$$\mathbf{n} = \frac{\mathbf{x}}{\|\mathbf{x}\|} = \frac{\mathbf{\Phi}_u \times \mathbf{\Phi}_v}{\|\mathbf{\Phi}_u \times \mathbf{\Phi}_v\|}. \tag{8.2.1}$$

There will, of course, be two unit normal vector fields, $\mathbf{n}$ and $-\mathbf{n}$, both perpendicular to S but pointing in opposite directions. The choice of unit normal vector will determine the orientation of the surface.

Now imagine S sits in a vector field $\mathbf{v}(x, y, z)$, a moving fluid, for example. We want to measure how much fluid passes through S per unit time, a quantity known as the flux of the fluid through the surface. The surface integral of $\mathbf{v}$ over S tells us the flux. We need $\mathbf{n}$ because we want to add up, across S, the component of $\mathbf{v}$ perpendicular to the surface and in the direction of $\mathbf{n}$. The surface integral is given by

$$\text{Flux} = \iint\limits_S \mathbf{v} \cdot d\mathbf{S} = \iint\limits_S \mathbf{v} \cdot \mathbf{n} dS, \tag{8.2.2}$$

where $\mathbf{v} \cdot \mathbf{n} dS$ represents the flux through an infinitesimal area dS of S.

Using (8.2.1), we can rewrite (8.2.2) as

$$\iint\limits_S \mathbf{v} \cdot d\mathbf{S} = \iint\limits_S \mathbf{v} \cdot \frac{\mathbf{\Phi}_u \times \mathbf{\Phi}_v}{\|\mathbf{\Phi}_u \times \mathbf{\Phi}_v\|} dS. \tag{8.2.3}$$

Before looking at how vector surface integrals relate to differential forms, we need one more piece of information – a formula for dS. Figure 8.3 shows an arbitrary point $P(u_0, v_0)$, with position vector $\mathbf{\Phi}(u_0, v_0)$, on S. If we increase u_0 to $u_0 + \Delta u$, and increase v_0 to $v_0 + \Delta v$, vector $\mathbf{\Phi}(u, v)$ will sweep out a little patch ΔS of the surface S. We can approximate the area of ΔS by the area of the parallelogram – in the tangent plane to S at $P(u_0, v_0)$ – spanned by the two vectors $\mathbf{\Phi}_u \Delta u$ and $\mathbf{\Phi}_v \Delta v$. The area of this parallelogram is given by magnitude of the cross product of $\mathbf{\Phi}_u \Delta u$ and $\mathbf{\Phi}_v \Delta v$, ie

$$\|\mathbf{\Phi}_u \Delta u \times \mathbf{\Phi}_v \Delta v\| = \|\mathbf{\Phi}_u \times \mathbf{\Phi}_v\| \, \Delta u \, \Delta v.$$

As we make Δu and Δv smaller, the area of the parallelogram becomes a better approximation to the area of ΔS until eventually we can say

$$dS = \|\mathbf{\Phi}_u \times \mathbf{\Phi}_v\| \, du \, dv,$$

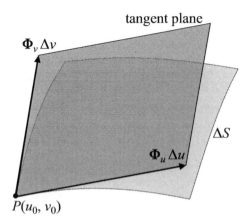

Figure 8.3: Approximating ΔS by a parallelogram in the tangent plane.

and (8.2.3) can be rewritten as

$$\iint\limits_{S} \mathbf{v} \cdot d\mathbf{S} = \iint\limits_{D} \mathbf{v} \cdot (\mathbf{\Phi}_u \times \mathbf{\Phi}_v)\, dA, \tag{8.2.4}$$

where $dA = du\, dv$ and D is some region of the uv plane.

Example 8.2. From Math Insight [13]. Integrate the vector field $\mathbf{v}(x, y, z) = 2x\hat{\mathbf{e}}_x + 2y\hat{\mathbf{e}}_y + 2z\hat{\mathbf{e}}_z$ over the surface S of a cylinder given by $x^2 + y^2 = 9$ for $0 \le z \le 5$. This is a cylinder of radius 3 and height 5 sitting on the xy plane. We are only concerned with the side of the cylinder, not the top and bottom. There are two orientations for this surface, corresponding to inward and outward pointing normal vectors. We'll use the outward pointing orientation, ie we are considering flux moving from inside to outside of the cylinder.

We can parameterise S using $\mathbf{\Phi}(u, v) = 3\cos u\hat{\mathbf{e}}_x + 3\sin u\hat{\mathbf{e}}_y + v\hat{\mathbf{e}}_z$ for $0 \le u \le 2\pi$ and $0 \le v \le 5$.

First, we need to express the vector field $\mathbf{v}$ in terms of u and v:

$$\mathbf{v}(\mathbf{\Phi}(u, v)) = 6\cos u\hat{\mathbf{e}}_x + 6\sin u\hat{\mathbf{e}}_y + 2v\hat{\mathbf{e}}_z$$

$$= (6\cos u, 6\sin u, 2v).$$

Next, we find the tangent vectors to S, which are

$$\mathbf{\Phi}_u = \frac{\partial \mathbf{\Phi}}{\partial u} = (-3\sin u, 3\cos u, 0)$$

and

$$\mathbf{\Phi}_v = \frac{\partial \mathbf{\Phi}}{\partial v} = (0,0,1)\,.$$

The cross product $\mathbf{\Phi}_u \times \mathbf{\Phi}_v$ is found using a version of (1.6.2)

$$\mathbf{\Phi}_u \times \mathbf{\Phi}_v = \begin{vmatrix} \mathbf{i} & \mathbf{j} & \mathbf{k} \\ -3\sin u & 3\cos u & 0 \\ 0 & 0 & 1 \end{vmatrix}$$

$$= 3\cos u\,\hat{\mathbf{e}}_x + 3\sin u\,\hat{\mathbf{e}}_y + 0\hat{\mathbf{e}}_z$$

$$= (3\cos u, 3\sin u, 0)\,.$$

We can verify this is an outward pointing normal vector by plugging in a specific point. An easy one is $u = 0$, $v = 0$, which corresponds to the xyz point $(3,0,0)$. This gives a normal vector $(3,0,0)$, which is indeed an outward pointing normal vector.

The total flux through S is then given by (8.2.4)

$$\iint\limits_S \mathbf{v} \cdot d\mathbf{S} = \iint\limits_D \mathbf{v} \cdot (\mathbf{\Phi}_u \times \mathbf{\Phi}_v)\, dA$$

$$= \int_0^5 \int_0^{2\pi} (6\cos u, 6\sin u, 2v) \cdot (3\cos u, 3\sin u, 0)\, du\, dv$$

$$= \int_0^5 \int_0^{2\pi} \left(18\cos^2 u + 18\sin^2 u\right) du\, dv$$

$$= \int_0^5 \int_0^{2\pi} 18\, du\, dv$$

$$= 180\pi.$$

If we wanted to change the orientation of our surface in order to find the total flux moving across S from outside to inside of the cylinder, we would use an inward pointing normal vector, ie $(-3\cos u, -3\sin u, 0)$. The answer would then, unsurprisingly, come out as -180π.

8.2.1 And with differential forms ...

We start with the 2-form $\omega_2 = f_1\, dy \wedge dz + f_2\, dz \wedge dx + f_3\, dx \wedge dy$ that we know is associated, in a surfacey way, with the vector field $\mathbf{v}(x,y,z) = f_1\hat{\mathbf{e}}_x + f_2\hat{\mathbf{e}}_y + f_3\hat{\mathbf{e}}_z$. We want to integrate ω_2 over a surface S, where S is defined by the vector equation

$$\mathbf{\Phi}(u,v) = x(u,v)\,\hat{\mathbf{e}}_x + y(u,v)\,\hat{\mathbf{e}}_y + z(u,v)\,\hat{\mathbf{e}}_z\,.$$

The tangent vectors to S are

$$\mathbf{\Phi}_u = \frac{\partial \mathbf{\Phi}}{\partial u} = \left(\frac{\partial x}{\partial u}, \frac{\partial y}{\partial u}, \frac{\partial z}{\partial u}\right)$$

and

$$\mathbf{\Phi}_v = \frac{\partial \mathbf{\Phi}}{\partial v} = \left(\frac{\partial x}{\partial v}, \frac{\partial y}{\partial v}, \frac{\partial z}{\partial v} \right).$$

A version of (7.2.4) tells us that the basis 2-form $dy \wedge dz$ acts on tangents vectors $\frac{\partial \mathbf{\Phi}}{\partial u}$ and $\frac{\partial \mathbf{\Phi}}{\partial v}$ as

$$(dy \wedge dz)\left(\frac{\partial \mathbf{\Phi}}{\partial u}, \frac{\partial \mathbf{\Phi}}{\partial v} \right) = \begin{vmatrix} \frac{\partial y}{\partial u} & \frac{\partial y}{\partial v} \\ \frac{\partial z}{\partial u} & \frac{\partial z}{\partial v} \end{vmatrix}.$$

And the basis 2-form $dz \wedge dx$ acts on tangents vectors $\frac{\partial \mathbf{\Phi}}{\partial u}$ and $\frac{\partial \mathbf{\Phi}}{\partial v}$ as

$$(dz \wedge dx)\left(\frac{\partial \mathbf{\Phi}}{\partial u}, \frac{\partial \mathbf{\Phi}}{\partial v} \right) = \begin{vmatrix} \frac{\partial z}{\partial u} & \frac{\partial z}{\partial v} \\ \frac{\partial x}{\partial u} & \frac{\partial x}{\partial v} \end{vmatrix}.$$

And the basis 2-form $dx \wedge dy$ acts on tangents vectors $\frac{\partial \mathbf{\Phi}}{\partial u}$ and $\frac{\partial \mathbf{\Phi}}{\partial v}$ as

$$(dx \wedge dy)\left(\frac{\partial \mathbf{\Phi}}{\partial u}, \frac{\partial \mathbf{\Phi}}{\partial v} \right) = \begin{vmatrix} \frac{\partial x}{\partial u} & \frac{\partial x}{\partial v} \\ \frac{\partial y}{\partial u} & \frac{\partial y}{\partial v} \end{vmatrix}.$$

Plug these into (7.2.3)

$$\int_S \omega_2 = \int_D \omega_2 \left(\frac{\partial \mathbf{\Phi}}{\partial u}, \frac{\partial \mathbf{\Phi}}{\partial v} \right) du\, dv$$

and we get

$$\int_S \omega_2 = \int_D \left(f_1 \begin{vmatrix} \frac{\partial y}{\partial u} & \frac{\partial y}{\partial v} \\ \frac{\partial z}{\partial u} & \frac{\partial z}{\partial v} \end{vmatrix} + f_2 \begin{vmatrix} \frac{\partial z}{\partial u} & \frac{\partial z}{\partial v} \\ \frac{\partial x}{\partial u} & \frac{\partial x}{\partial v} \end{vmatrix} + f_3 \begin{vmatrix} \frac{\partial x}{\partial u} & \frac{\partial x}{\partial v} \\ \frac{\partial y}{\partial u} & \frac{\partial y}{\partial v} \end{vmatrix} \right) du\, dv$$

$$= \int_D \left(f_1 \left(\frac{\partial y}{\partial u} \frac{\partial z}{\partial v} - \frac{\partial y}{\partial v} \frac{\partial z}{\partial u} \right) + f_2 \left(\frac{\partial z}{\partial u} \frac{\partial x}{\partial v} - \frac{\partial z}{\partial v} \frac{\partial x}{\partial u} \right) + f_3 \left(\frac{\partial x}{\partial u} \frac{\partial y}{\partial v} - \frac{\partial x}{\partial v} \frac{\partial y}{\partial u} \right) \right) du\, dv.$$

$$(8.2.5)$$

But those terms in brackets are (check it out using (1.6.1)) the cross product $\mathbf{\Phi}_u \times \mathbf{\Phi}_v$ of the tangent vectors

$$\frac{\partial \mathbf{\Phi}}{\partial u} = \mathbf{\Phi}_u$$

and

$$\frac{\partial \mathbf{\Phi}}{\partial v} = \mathbf{\Phi}_v.$$

Thus, we have shown that (8.2.5) is equivalent to the vector calculus formula (8.2.4) for the surface integral

$$\iint_S \mathbf{v} \cdot d\mathbf{S} = \iint_D \mathbf{v} \cdot (\mathbf{\Phi}_u \times \mathbf{\Phi}_v)\, dA,$$

in other words,

$$\int_S \omega_2 = \iint_S \mathbf{v} \cdot d\mathbf{S}. \tag{8.2.6}$$

From section 5.2 we know that $d\omega_1$ (where ω_1 is a 1-form) is associated with the curl vector field $\nabla \times \mathbf{v}$, so we can also write (8.2.6) as

$$\int_S d\omega_1 = \iint_S (\nabla \times \mathbf{v}) \cdot d\mathbf{S}.$$

8.3 Volume integrals

An integral that is evaluated over a volume is called a volume integral. The volume integral of a scalar field ϕ over a region M is denoted by

$$\iiint_M \phi \, dV,$$

and is a scalar. The volume integral of a vector field $\mathbf{v}$ over a region M is denoted by

$$\iiint_M \mathbf{v} dV,$$

and is a vector. In both cases, dV is the volume element, which in Cartesian coordinates is given by

$$dV = dx \, dy \, dz. \tag{8.3.1}$$

So the volume integral of a function $f(x, y, z)$ over a region M is given by

$$\iiint_M f \, dV = \iiint_M f \, dx \, dy \, dz.$$

If f is a function that gives the density of the region M, then

$$\iiint_M f \, dx \, dy \, dz$$

gives the mass of M.

So if M is the unit cube defined by $0 \le x \le 1$, $0 \le y \le 1$, $0 \le z \le 1$ and the density function is $f = x^2 + y^2 + z^2$, then the mass of M is given by

$$\iiint_M f \, dx \, dy \, dz = \int_0^1 \int_0^1 \int_0^1 \left(x^2 + y^2 + z^2 \right) dx \, dy \, dz$$

$$= 1.$$

8.3.1 And with differential forms ...

This is straightforward. The volume element $dV = dx\,dy\,dz$ corresponds to the basis 3-form $dx \wedge dy \wedge dz$. And we can therefore write, for the 3-form $\omega_3 = f\,dx \wedge dy \wedge dz$,

$$\iiint_M f\,dV = \int_M \omega_3.$$

And, from section 5.3, we know we can associate the exterior derivative $d\omega_2$ (where ω_2 is a 2-form) with the divergence $\nabla \cdot \mathbf{v}$. So if we substitute $\nabla \cdot \mathbf{v}$ for f we get

$$\iiint_M \nabla \cdot \mathbf{v}\,dV = \int_M d\omega_2.$$

Table 8.1 summarises the relationships between the integrals of vector calculus and their equivalent differential forms. Recall that the 1-form $\omega_1 = f_1\,dx + f_2\,dy + f_3\,dz$, the 2-form $\omega_2 = f_1\,dy \wedge dz + f_2\,dz \wedge dx + f_3\,dx \wedge dy$ and the 3-form $\omega_3 = f\,dx \wedge dy \wedge dz$.

vector calculus	differential forms
$\displaystyle\int_C \mathbf{v} \cdot d\boldsymbol{\Phi}$	$\displaystyle\int_C \omega_1$
$\displaystyle\int_C \nabla f \cdot d\boldsymbol{\Phi}$	$\displaystyle\int_C df$
$\displaystyle\iint_S \mathbf{v} \cdot d\mathbf{S}$	$\displaystyle\int_S \omega_2$
$\displaystyle\iint_S (\nabla \times \mathbf{v}) \cdot d\mathbf{S}$	$\displaystyle\int_S d\omega_1$
$\displaystyle\iiint_M f\,dV$	$\displaystyle\int_M \omega_3$
$\displaystyle\iiint_M \nabla \cdot \mathbf{v}\,dV$	$\displaystyle\int_M d\omega_2$

Table 8.1: Vector calculus integrals and equivalent differential forms.

9 The generalised Stokes' theorem

And now the big one, our mathematical El Dorado; namely, the generalised Stokes' theorem, which relates integrals over a manifold of – rather wonderfully – *any* dimension with integrals over the boundary of that manifold.

Lee [12] remarks that the generalised Stokes' theorem is:

> the central result in the theory of integration on manifolds ... It is a far-reaching generalization of the fundamental theorem of calculus and of the classical theorems of vector calculus.

(We won't go there, but the dedicated reader can find a reasonably accessible proof of the generalised Stokes' theorem in Schulz and Schulz [18].)

Differential forms allow us to understand the four integral theorems of vector calculus:

- the gradient theorem,

- Green's theorem,

- Stokes' theorem,

- and the divergence theorem

as special cases of a single unifying theorem – the generalised Stokes' theorem:

$$\int_M d\omega = \int_{\partial M} \omega. \tag{9.0.1}$$

Here M is a smooth oriented k-dimensional manifold, ∂M is the properly oriented boundary of M, and ω is a $k - 1$ differential form. Remember that the boundary of a k-dimensional manifold, assuming one exists, is itself a manifold of dimension $k - 1$. So in $\mathbb{R}^2$ a two-dimensional unit disk S has a boundary ∂S, which is the (one-dimensional) unit circle. And in $\mathbb{R}^3$ a three-dimensional solid ball M has a boundary ∂M, which is a (two-dimensional) sphere. The meaning of 'properly oriented boundary' should become clearer in the following discussion.

The relevant constituents of the four vector calculus integral theorems as related to the generalised Stokes' theorem are summarised in Table 9.1.

	$\mathbb{R}^n$	M	∂M	ω	$d\omega$
gradient theorem	$\mathbb{R}^2/\mathbb{R}^3$	curve C	two endpoints	0-form	1-form
Green's theorem	$\mathbb{R}^2/\mathbb{R}^3$	surface S	closed curve	1-form	2-form
Stokes' theorem	$\mathbb{R}^3$	surface S	closed curve	1-form	2-form
divergence theorem	$\mathbb{R}^3$	volume V	closed surface	2-form	3-form

Table 9.1: The four vector calculus integral theorems.

So, for example, the gradient theorem takes place in $\mathbb{R}^2$ or $\mathbb{R}^3$, where M is a curve C, the boundary ∂M of M are the two endpoints of C, the differential form ω is a 0-form (ie a smooth function) and $d\omega$ is a 1-form. And the divergence theorem takes place in $\mathbb{R}^3$, where M is a volume V, the boundary ∂M of M is the closed surface surrounding V, the differential form ω is a 2-form and $d\omega$ is a 3-form.

We'll now look at the above four theorems in turn and show how each is a special case of the generalised Stokes' theorem.

9.1 The gradient theorem

We've already met the gradient theorem (8.1.3)

$$\int_C \nabla f \cdot d\mathbf{\Phi} = f\left(\mathbf{\Phi}\left(b\right)\right) - f\left(\mathbf{\Phi}\left(a\right)\right),$$

which states that in order to evaluate the line integral of a conservative vector field $\mathbf{v} = \nabla f$, we only need to know the value of f at the endpoints of the curve C.

9.1.1 Generalised Stokes' theorem ...

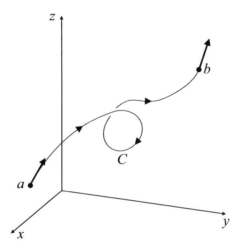

Figure 9.1: Oriented curve C between points a and b.

Let the 0-form $\omega = f\left(x, y, z\right).$ Using the generalised Stokes' theorem (9.0.1)

$$\int_M d\omega = \int_{\partial M} \omega,$$

we have $M = C$, and the boundary ∂M of C is a 0-dimensional manifold consisting of the curve's endpoints a and b. (A 0-dimensional manifold is a set of discrete points.) Taking the left side of the generalised Stokes' theorem first, we can write

$$\int_C d\omega = \int_C df$$

$$= \int_C \frac{\partial f}{\partial x} dx + \frac{\partial f}{\partial y} dy + \frac{\partial f}{\partial z} dz. \tag{9.1.1}$$

Using (8.1.4)

$$\int_C \mathbf{v} \cdot d\mathbf{\Phi} = \int_C f_1 \, dx + f_2 \, dy + f_3 \, dz,$$

and the definition of the gradient from section 5.1, we can write (9.1.1) as

$$\int_C d\omega = \int_C \nabla f \cdot d\mathbf{\Phi}.$$

Next, the right side of the generalised Stokes' theorem:

$$\int_{\partial M} \omega = \int_{\partial C} f,$$

which represents the slightly weird notion of an integral of a 0-form f over a 0-dimensional manifold ∂C. The interpretation of this integral is that it is the sum of values of f acting on the endpoints a and b. However, points a and b inherit an orientation from the curve C, as shown in Figure 9.1. A tangent vector at a is pointing 'into' C, giving a a negative orientation. A tangent vector at b is pointing 'outside of' C, giving b a positive orientation. In other words, the boundary points a and b are oriented plus or minus depending on whether the oriented curve C goes into or out of each point. We therefore can say

$$\int_{\partial C} f = f\left(\boldsymbol{\Phi}\left(b\right)\right) - f\left(\boldsymbol{\Phi}\left(a\right)\right),$$

and we have recovered the gradient theorem from the generalised Stokes' theorem.

9.2 Green's theorem

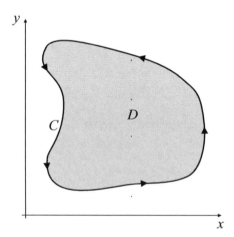

Figure 9.2: Oriented boundary C of a region D.

Green's theorem relates a line integral along a closed curve with the double integral of a vector field in the plane. If $\mathbf{v}\left(x, y\right) = f_1\left(x, y\right)\hat{\mathbf{e}}_x + f_2\left(x, y\right)\hat{\mathbf{e}}_y$ is a vector field and C

is a positively oriented, simple (ie it doesn't cross itself) curve enclosing some region D in the xy plane – see Figure 9.2 – then Green's theorem states

$$\int_C f_1 \, dx + f_2 \, dy = \iint_D \left(\frac{\partial f_2}{\partial x} - \frac{\partial f_1}{\partial y} \right) dx \, dy.$$

Using (8.1.4)

$$\int_C \mathbf{v} \cdot d\mathbf{\Phi} = \int_C f_1 \, dx + f_2 \, dy + f_3 \, dz,$$

we can also write Green's theorem as

$$\int_C \mathbf{v} \cdot d\mathbf{\Phi} = \iint_D \left(\frac{\partial f_2}{\partial x} - \frac{\partial f_1}{\partial y} \right) dx \, dy.$$

We are following the convention that the boundary C has a positive orientation if it is traced out in a counterclockwise direction.

9.2.1 Generalised Stokes' theorem ...

Let the 1-form $\omega = f_1 \, dx + f_2 \, dy$. Using the generalised Stokes' theorem (9.0.1)

$$\int_M d\omega = \int_{\partial M} \omega,$$

we can write $(\partial M = C, \, M = D)$

$$\int_D d\omega = \int_C f_1 \, dx + f_2 \, dy$$

$$\int_D d\omega = \int_C \mathbf{v} \cdot d\mathbf{\Phi}.$$

And then

$$\int_D d\omega = \int_D d \left(f_1 \, dx + f_2 \, dy \right).$$

This is a simpler version (there's no dz) of the curl calculation we looked at in section 5.2. We get

$$\int_D d\omega = \int_D \left(\frac{\partial f_1}{\partial y} dy \wedge dx + \frac{\partial f_2}{\partial x} dx \wedge dy \right)$$

$$= \int_D \left(\frac{\partial f_2}{\partial x} - \frac{\partial f_1}{\partial y} \right) dx \wedge dy,$$

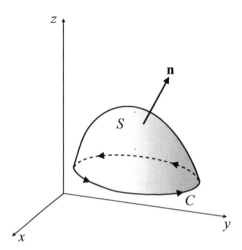

Figure 9.3: Oriented boundary C of a surface S.

where we've changed the sign of the $\frac{\partial f_1}{\partial y}\,dy \wedge dx$ term to get the differentials in the correct order. We can now write this as the ordinary (ie unoriented) double integral

$$= \iint\limits_{D} \left(\frac{\partial f_2}{\partial x} - \frac{\partial f_1}{\partial y} \right) dx\,dy,$$

which is what we set out to show.

9.3 Stokes' theorem

Green's theorem relates a line integral to a double integral over a planar region. Stokes' theorem – which can be regarded as a three-dimensional version of Green's theorem – relates a line integral to a surface integral. Specifically, Stokes' theorem relates the line integral of a vector field around the boundary of a surface with the surface integral of the curl of that vector field. Recall that a surface integral, which measures the amount of vector field 'stuff' passing through a surface S per unit time, is given by (8.2.2)

$$\text{Flux} = \iint\limits_{S} \mathbf{v} \cdot d\mathbf{S} = \iint\limits_{S} \mathbf{v} \cdot \mathbf{n}dS.$$

In Stokes' theorem we're taking the surface integral not of $\mathbf{v}$ but of another vector field – the curl of $\mathbf{v}$. So if $\mathbf{v}\,(x,y,z) = f_1\,(x,y,z)\,\hat{\mathbf{e}}_x + f_2\,(x,y,z)\,\hat{\mathbf{e}}_y + f_3\,(x,y,z)\,\hat{\mathbf{e}}_z$ is a vector field and C is a positively oriented simple curve enclosing an oriented surface

S – see Figure 9.3 – then Stokes' theorem states

$$\int_C \mathbf{v} \cdot d\mathbf{\Phi} = \iint_S \operatorname{curl} \mathbf{v} \cdot d\mathbf{S} = \iint_S \operatorname{curl} \mathbf{v} \cdot \mathbf{n} dS.$$

In words, Stokes' theorem says that the line integral of the tangential component of a vector field $\mathbf{v}$ around C is equal to the surface integral of the normal component of the curl of $\mathbf{v}$ taken over S.

We need to ensure that the orientation of the surface S (determined by the choice of normal vector $\mathbf{n}$) matches the orientation of the boundary C. The rule is that the direction of C is considered positive if you are walking around C with your head pointing in the direction of $\mathbf{n}$ and the surface is on your left.

Note that the integral remains the same for any surface S as long as we keep the same boundary curve C.

Using (8.1.4)

$$\int_C \mathbf{v} \cdot d\mathbf{\Phi} = \int_C f_1 \, dx + f_2 \, dy + f_3 \, dz,$$

we can also write Stokes' theorem as

$$\int_C f_1 \, dx + f_2 \, dy + f_3 \, dz = \iint_S \operatorname{curl} \mathbf{v} \cdot d\mathbf{S} = \iint_S \operatorname{curl} \mathbf{v} \cdot \mathbf{n} dS.$$

9.3.1 Generalised Stokes' theorem ...

The derivation is similar to that for Green's theorem, except we are using three dimensions instead of two. Let the 1-form $\omega = f_1 \, dx + f_2 \, dy + f_3 \, dz$. Using the generalised Stokes' theorem (9.0.1)

$$\int_M d\omega = \int_{\partial M} \omega,$$

we can write ($\partial M = C$, $M = S$)

$$\int_S d\omega = \int_C f_1 \, dx + f_2 \, dy + f_3 \, dz$$

$$\int_S d\omega = \int_C \mathbf{v} \cdot d\mathbf{\Phi}.$$

And then

$$\int_S d\omega = \int_S d \left(f_1 \, dx + f_2 \, dy + f_3 \, dz \right).$$

Again referring back to the curl calculation we looked at in section 5.2, we find

$$\int_S d\omega = \int_S \left(\frac{\partial f_3}{\partial y} - \frac{\partial f_2}{\partial z} \right) dy \wedge dz + \int_S \left(\frac{\partial f_1}{\partial z} - \frac{\partial f_3}{\partial x} \right) dz \wedge dx + \int_S \left(\frac{\partial f_2}{\partial x} - \frac{\partial f_1}{\partial y} \right) dx \wedge dy,$$

which we can write as the ordinary (ie unoriented) double integral

$$= \iint_S \left(\frac{\partial f_3}{\partial y} - \frac{\partial f_2}{\partial z} \right) dy \, dz + \iint_S \left(\frac{\partial f_1}{\partial z} - \frac{\partial f_3}{\partial x} \right) dz \, dx + \iint_S \left(\frac{\partial f_2}{\partial x} - \frac{\partial f_1}{\partial y} \right) dx \, dy.$$

Using the correspondence (3.3.1)

$$dy \wedge dz \Leftrightarrow \hat{\mathbf{e}}_x, \ dz \wedge dx \Leftrightarrow \hat{\mathbf{e}}_y, \ dx \wedge dy \Leftrightarrow \hat{\mathbf{e}}_z,$$

and the equation for curl (5.2.1), we have

$$\int_S d\omega = \iint_S \operatorname{curl} \mathbf{v} \cdot d\mathbf{S},$$

which is what we set out to show.

9.4 Divergence theorem

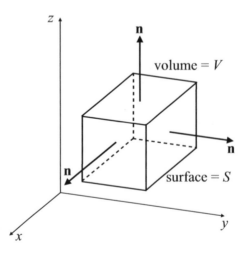

Figure 9.4: Volume V and outward oriented boundary surface S.

The divergence theorem relates a surface integral to a volume integral. Specifically, the divergence theorem relates the divergence of a vector field within a volume to the outward flux of the vector field through the surface enclosing that volume. Let V be a three-dimensional region surrounded by a closed surface S, where S has an outward (ie positive) orientation. If $\mathbf{v}\,(x, y, z) = f_1\,(x, y, z)\,\hat{\mathbf{e}}_x + f_2\,(x, y, z)\,\hat{\mathbf{e}}_y + f_3\,(x, y, z)\,\hat{\mathbf{e}}_z$ is a vector field – see Figure 9.4 – then the divergence theorem states

$$\iint_S \mathbf{v} \cdot d\mathbf{S} = \iiint_V \operatorname{div} \mathbf{v} dV.$$

In words, the divergence theorem says that the surface integral of the normal component of a vector field $\mathbf{v}$ through a closed surface S is equal to the integral of the divergence of $\mathbf{v}$ taken over the volume V enclosed by the surface.

The divergence theorem allows us to choose between evaluating a double or a triple integral. Say, for example, we wanted to find the surface integral depicted in Figure 9.4. The divergence theorem would be useful as it is almost certainly easier to integrate over the box-shaped region V than to take the surface integral of each of the six faces that constitute S.

9.4.1 Generalised Stokes' theorem ...

We start with the 2-form $\omega = f_1\,dy \wedge dz + f_2\,dz \wedge dx + f_3\,dx \wedge dy$ that we know is associated with the vector field $\mathbf{v}\,(x, y, z) = f_1\hat{\mathbf{e}}_x + f_2\hat{\mathbf{e}}_y + f_3\hat{\mathbf{e}}_z$. We know from (8.2.6) that

$$\int_S \omega = \iint_S \mathbf{v} \cdot d\mathbf{S}.$$

Using the generalised Stokes' theorem (9.0.1)

$$\int_M d\omega = \int_{\partial M} \omega,$$

we can write $(\partial M = S,\ M = V)$

$$\int_V d\omega = \int_S f_1\,dy \wedge dz + f_2\,dz \wedge dx + f_3\,dx \wedge dy$$

$$\int_V d\omega = \iint_S \mathbf{v} \cdot d\mathbf{S}.$$

And then

$$\int_V d\omega = \int_V d\,(f_1\,dy \wedge dz + f_2\,dz \wedge dx + f_3\,dx \wedge dy)\,.$$

Equation (5.3.3) tells us the exterior derivative of the 2-form $f_1\,dy \wedge dz + f_2\,dz \wedge dx + f_3\,dx \wedge dy$ is given by

$$\int_V d\omega = \left(\frac{\partial f_1}{\partial x} + \frac{\partial f_2}{\partial y} + \frac{\partial f_3}{\partial z}\right) dx \wedge dy \wedge dz.$$

Using the equation for divergence (5.3.1) and the volume element (8.3.1)

$$dV = dx\,dy\,dz,$$

which corresponds to the basis 3-form

$$dx \wedge dy \wedge dz,$$

we have

$$\int_V d\omega = \iiint_V \operatorname{div} \mathbf{v}\,dV,$$

which is what we set out to show.

10 Maxwell's equations

Maxwell's four famous equations constitute the foundation of classical electromagnetic theory. They relate the electric field $\mathbf{E} = (E_x, E_y, E_z)$ and the magnetic field $\mathbf{B} = (B_x, B_y, B_z)$, to charge density ρ (charge per unit volume) and current density $\mathbf{J}$ (current per unit area – a vector). There are also a couple of physical constants: the permittivity of free space ϵ_0, and the permeability of free space μ_0. Maxwell was able to use his equations to show that light travels at a fixed speed v in empty space, where

$$v = \frac{1}{\sqrt{\epsilon_0 \mu_0}} = 3.00 \times 10^8 \, \text{m/s}.$$

Penrose [17] comments:

> Maxwell's theory had gained in strength, not only because of the powerful support it obtained from observation ... but also because of the compelling and unifying nature of the theory itself, whereby the laws governing electric fields, magnetic fields, and light are all subsumed into a mathematical scheme of remarkable elegance and essential simplicity.

In the early years of the twentieth century, Einstein built on Maxwell's work when developing his theory of special relativity.

As we'll see shortly, in flat spacetime differential forms neatly reduce Maxwell's four equations to just two concise formulations:

$$d\mathsf{F} = 0$$

and

$$d \star \mathsf{F} = \mathsf{J},$$

where F is a 2-form called the electromagnetic tensor, and J is something called the current 3-form.

10.1 The vector calculus approach

But first we need to familiarise ourselves with the four classical vector calculus Maxwell's equations – what they are and what they describe. Here are the eponymous equations.

$$\nabla \cdot \mathbf{E} = \frac{\rho}{\epsilon_0} \quad \text{Gauss's law,}$$

$$\nabla \cdot \mathbf{B} = 0 \quad \text{Gauss's law for magnetism,}$$

$$\nabla \times \mathbf{E} = -\frac{\partial \mathbf{B}}{\partial t} \quad \text{Faraday's law,}$$

$$\nabla \times \mathbf{B} = \mu_0 \mathbf{J} + \mu_0 \epsilon_0 \frac{\partial \mathbf{E}}{\partial t} \quad \text{Ampère-Maxwell law.}$$

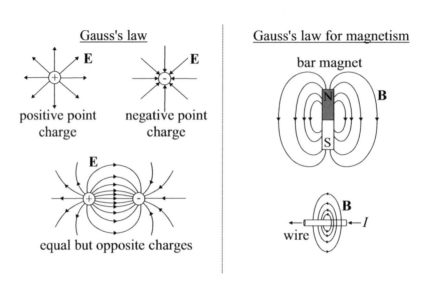

Figure 10.1: Maxwell's equations – the first pair.

We can conveniently divide Maxwell's equations into two pairs. The first pair – Gauss's law and Gauss's law for magnetism – describe the divergence of the electric field and magnetic field. The second pair – Faraday's law and the Ampère-Maxwell law – describe the curl of the electric field $\mathbf{E}$ and magnetic field $\mathbf{B}$, and also how these two fields are related. Referring to Figure 10.1:

- Gauss's law says the divergence of a static electric field $\mathbf{E}$ is proportional to the charge density at that point. At a positively charged point the divergence is positive, ie the field lines flow out of the point. At a negatively charged point the divergence is negative, ie the field lines flow into the point.

- Gauss's law for magnetism says at any point the divergence of a magnetic field $\mathbf{B}$ is zero. This is because there are no isolated magnetic poles. Therefore, magnetic field lines always form closed loops, running from the north to south pole of a magnet, or circling a current-carrying wire. This is different to static electric field lines, which always flow from a positive charge to a negative charge and never form closed loops.

On to the second pair of Maxwell's equations. Referring to Figure 10.2:

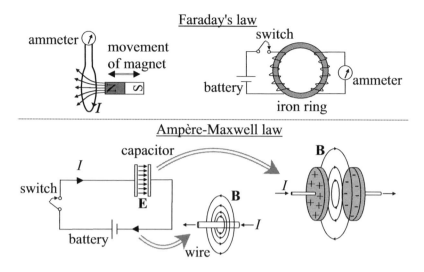

Figure 10.2: Maxwell's equations – the second pair.

- Faraday's law says a changing magnetic field induces an electric field. Moving a magnet through a loop or coil of wire, for example, produces an electric field which induces a current I to flow through the wire. Faraday himself conducted a famous experiment involving two coils of wire wrapped around a soft iron ring. He connected one coil to a battery, creating an electromagnet. When he closed or opened the switch, a changing magnetic field was momentarily created that induced a current to flow in the other coil.

- The Ampère-Maxwell law says that circulating magnetic fields are produced by an electric current *and* by a changing electric field. In other words, there are two magnetic field sources on the right side of the Ampère-Maxwell equation. A simple charging capacitor circuit provides a good example of both phenomena (a capacitor is a device for storing electrical charge). When the switch is closed, current flows until the capacitor is fully charged. This current – represented by $\mathbf{J}$, the current density, the first source – produces a magnetic field around the wire. At the same time, as the capacitor charges, a changing electric field is produced between the capacitor plates. This electric field also generates a magnetic field. No current flows between the plates. However, the magnetic field is the same as if a current did actually flow. Because the $\epsilon_0 \frac{\partial \mathbf{E}}{\partial t}$ term – the second source – behaves like a current, Maxwell called it the displacement current.

Maxwell's equations in the differential form given above apply to *points* in space and time. Sometimes it's more useful to solve problems by integrating over curves, surfaces and volumes. To do this we need the equivalent integral forms of Maxwell's equations, which can be obtained by applying the divergence theorem (to the first pair of equations) and Stokes' theorems (to the second pair).

10.2 The differential forms approach

Relativity theory unifies space and time into a single four-dimensional manifold called spacetime. Special relativity is a theory of flat spacetime (known as Minkowski space – Hermann Minkowski was a mathematician and Einstein's teacher), which we can describe using our usual Cartesian x, y, z coordinates plus a time t coordinate. In flat spacetime, using differential forms, Maxwell's equations can be written ultra-compactly as

$$d\mathsf{F} = 0$$

and

$$d \star \mathsf{F} = \mathsf{J}.$$

Bachman [5] comments:

> The differential form version of Maxwell's Equation has a huge advantage over the vector formulation: It is coordinate-free! A 2-form such as F is an operator that 'eats' pairs of vectors and 'spits out' numbers. The way it acts is completely geometric; that is, it can be defined without any reference to the coordinate system (t, x, y, z). This is especially poignant when one realizes that Maxwell's Equations are laws of nature that should not depend on a manmade construction such as coordinates.

10.2.1 The Hodge star operator

Before seeing how Maxwell's equations can be expressed in the language of differential forms, we need to briefly mention something called the Hodge star operator. We've seen how the wedge product allows us to multiply a p-form with a q-form to give a $(p + q)$-form. We've also seen how the exterior derivative operator d changes a k-form to a $(k + 1)$-form. The Hodge star operator is a linear function that converts a k-form in an n-dimensional space to an $(n - k)$-form. The Hodge star operator is denoted by a $\star$ immediately before the quantity to which it is applied. If we apply the Hodge star operator to a differential form ω, the result, $\star\omega$, is known as the Hodge dual.

In reasonably plain English, the Hodge star operator takes a k-form ω and converts it to a new $(n - k)$-form $\star\omega$ that contains the differentials missing in ω.

The formal definition of the Hodge star operator requires a metric tensor, a type of function that measures infinitesimal distances on a manifold. In Cartesian coordinates, however, where the metric tensor effectively consists of only ones and zeros, finding the Hodge dual is much more straightforward. In $\mathbb{R}^n$, for a basis k-form ω and a basis $(n - k)$-form $\star\omega$, we can then use the definition

$$\omega \wedge \star\omega = dx^1 \wedge dx^2 \cdots \wedge dx^n.$$

So in $\mathbb{R}^3$ the formula is

$$\omega \wedge \star\omega = dx \wedge dy \wedge dz.$$

For the basis 1-form $\omega = dx$, the missing differential are dy and dz, and therefore the Hodge dual $\star\omega = \star dx = dy \wedge dz$. As always, everything has to be in the correct order, so if $\omega = dy$, the missing differentials are dx and dz, and $\star\omega = \star dy = dz \wedge dx$ (because $dy \wedge dz \wedge dx = dx \wedge dy \wedge dz$).

The complete set of Hodge duals in $\mathbb{R}^3$ is as follows:

$$\star 1 = dx \wedge dy \wedge dz,$$

$$\star dx = dy \wedge dz, \;\; \star dy = dz \wedge dx, \;\; \star dz = dx \wedge dy,$$

$$\star(dx \wedge dy) = dz, \;\; \star(dz \wedge dx) = dy, \;\; \star(dy \wedge dz) = dx,$$

$$\star(dx \wedge dy \wedge dz) = 1.$$

When we come to write Gauss's law and the Ampère-Maxwell law in terms of differential forms, we'll be making use of $\star\mathsf{F}$, the Hodge dual of the 2-form F (the electromagnetic tensor), as well as $\star\mathsf{J}$, the Hodge dual of J, the current 3-form.

10.2.2 Moving on ...

We next simplify Maxwell's equations by absorbing the constants ϵ_0 and μ_0 into the units of calculation so that $\mu_0 = \epsilon_0 = 1$. The four equations can then be written as:

$$\nabla \cdot \mathbf{E} = \rho \;\; \text{Gauss's law,}$$

$$\nabla \cdot \mathbf{B} = 0 \;\; \text{Gauss's law for magnetism,}$$

$$\nabla \times \mathbf{E} + \frac{\partial \mathbf{B}}{\partial t} = 0 \;\; \text{Faraday's law,}$$

$$\nabla \times \mathbf{B} - \frac{\partial \mathbf{E}}{\partial t} = \mathbf{J} \;\; \text{Ampère-Maxwell law.}$$

In section 10.1, we conveniently divided Maxwell's equations into two pairs: Gauss's law and Gauss's law for magnetism, and Faraday's law and the Ampère-Maxwell law. However, a more natural pairing, and the one we'll be utilising from now on, is given by noting that Gauss's law for magnetism and Faraday's law

$$\nabla \cdot \mathbf{B} = 0 \;\; \nabla \times \mathbf{E} + \frac{\partial \mathbf{B}}{\partial t} = 0$$

look rather similar to Gauss's law and the Ampère-Maxwell law

$$\nabla \cdot \mathbf{E} = \rho \;\; \nabla \times \mathbf{B} - \frac{\partial \mathbf{E}}{\partial t} = \mathbf{J}.$$

This symmetry becomes even more apparent in a vacuum (where there is zero charge density ρ and zero current density $\mathbf{J}$), giving

$$\nabla \cdot \mathbf{B} = 0 \;\; \nabla \times \mathbf{E} + \frac{\partial \mathbf{B}}{\partial t} = 0$$

$$\nabla \cdot \mathbf{E} = 0 \quad \nabla \times \mathbf{B} - \frac{\partial \mathbf{E}}{\partial t} = 0.$$

Note that we can change the first equation to the second equation by substituting $\mathbf{E}$ for $\mathbf{B}$ and $-\mathbf{B}$ for $\mathbf{E}$, and vice versa. Baez and Muniain [6] state:

> This symmetry is called duality and is a clue that the electric and magnetic fields are part of a unified whole, the electromagnetic field.

Referring to the first pair of equations, we've seen that we can associate the exterior derivative of a 2-form with the divergence of a vector field (in this case $\nabla \cdot \mathbf{B}$). This is a hint that the magnetic field $\mathbf{B} = (B_x, B_y, B_z)$ can be naturally associated with a 2-form B, known as the magnetic field 2-form, where

$$\mathsf{B} = B_x dy \wedge dz + B_y dz \wedge dx + B_z dx \wedge dy.$$

We've also seen that we can associate the exterior derivative of a 1-form with the curl of a vector field (in this case $\nabla \times \mathbf{E}$). This is another hint, that the electric field $\mathbf{E} = (E_x, E_y, E_z)$ can be naturally associated with a 1-form E, known as the electric field 1-form, where

$$\mathsf{E} = E_x dx + E_y dy + E_z dz.$$

Quoting Baez and Muniain [6] again:

> The funny thing is that the second pair [of equations, ie $\nabla \cdot \mathbf{E} = 0$ and $\nabla \times \mathbf{B} - \frac{\partial \mathbf{E}}{\partial t} = 0$] seems to have the roles of E and B reversed (modulo the minus sign). This would amount to treating E as a 2-form and B as a 1-form! The Hodge star operator saves the day, since it converts 1-forms on 3-dimensional space into 2-forms, and vice versa.

The final ingredient in the mix is the requirement, already alluded to, that in order to describe the electromagnetic field in spacetime, E and B must be combined into a single fundamental entity, a 2-form F, called the electromagnetic tensor, where

$$\mathsf{F} = \mathsf{E} \wedge dt + \mathsf{B}$$

$$= E_x dx \wedge dt + E_y dy \wedge dt + E_z dz \wedge dt + B_x dy \wedge dz + B_y dz \wedge dx + B_z dx \wedge dy.$$

What follows is somewhat laborious, but persevere and eventually Maxwell's equations will emerge out of the mist.

10.2.3 Gauss's law for magnetism and Faraday's law

These two Maxwell equations are found by taking the exterior derivative of F, and then setting $d\mathsf{F} = 0$. Arfken et al. [3] comment:

> This equation [$d\mathsf{F} = 0$] is not a mathematical requirement on F; it is a statement of the physical properties of electric and magnetic fields.

So we say

$$dF = d(E \wedge dt + B)$$

$$= dE \wedge dt + dB$$

$$= \left(\frac{\partial E_x}{\partial x} dx + \frac{\partial E_x}{\partial y} dy + \frac{\partial E_x}{\partial z} dz + \frac{\partial E_x}{\partial t} dt \right) \wedge dx \wedge dt$$

$$+ \left(\frac{\partial E_y}{\partial x} dx + \frac{\partial E_y}{\partial y} dy + \frac{\partial E_y}{\partial z} dz + \frac{\partial E_y}{\partial t} dt \right) \wedge dy \wedge dt$$

$$+ \left(\frac{\partial E_z}{\partial x} dx + \frac{\partial E_z}{\partial y} dy + \frac{\partial E_z}{\partial z} dz + \frac{\partial E_z}{\partial t} dt \right) \wedge dz \wedge dt$$

$$+ \left(\frac{\partial B_x}{\partial x} dx + \frac{\partial B_x}{\partial y} dy + \frac{\partial B_x}{\partial z} dz + \frac{\partial B_x}{\partial t} dt \right) \wedge dy \wedge dz$$

$$+ \left(\frac{\partial B_y}{\partial x} dx + \frac{\partial B_y}{\partial y} dy + \frac{\partial B_y}{\partial z} dz + \frac{\partial B_y}{\partial t} dt \right) \wedge dz \wedge dx$$

$$+ \left(\frac{\partial B_z}{\partial x} dx + \frac{\partial B_z}{\partial y} dy + \frac{\partial B_z}{\partial z} dz + \frac{\partial B_z}{\partial t} dt \right) \wedge dx \wedge dy.$$

Many of these terms will drop out because $dx^i \wedge dx^i = 0$, and we get

$$= \left(\frac{\partial B_x}{\partial x} + \frac{\partial B_y}{\partial y} + \frac{\partial B_z}{\partial z} \right) dx \wedge dy \wedge dz + \frac{\partial B_x}{\partial t} dy \wedge dz \wedge dt + \frac{\partial B_y}{\partial t} dz \wedge dx \wedge dt$$

$$+ \frac{\partial B_z}{\partial t} dx \wedge dy \wedge dt + \frac{\partial E_z}{\partial y} dy \wedge dz \wedge dt + \frac{\partial E_y}{\partial z} dz \wedge dy \wedge dt + \frac{\partial E_x}{\partial z} dz \wedge dx \wedge dt$$

$$+ \frac{\partial E_z}{\partial x} dx \wedge dz \wedge dt + \frac{\partial E_y}{\partial x} dx \wedge dy \wedge dt + \frac{\partial E_x}{\partial y} dy \wedge dx \wedge dt$$

$$dF = \left(\frac{\partial B_x}{\partial x} + \frac{\partial B_y}{\partial y} + \frac{\partial B_z}{\partial z} \right) dx \wedge dy \wedge dz + \left[\left(\left[\frac{\partial E_z}{\partial y} - \frac{\partial E_y}{\partial z} \right] + \frac{\partial B_x}{\partial t} \right) dy \wedge dz \right.$$

$$\left. \left(\left[\frac{\partial E_x}{\partial z} - \frac{\partial E_z}{\partial x} \right] + \frac{\partial B_y}{\partial t} \right) dz \wedge dx + \left(\left[\frac{\partial E_y}{\partial x} - \frac{\partial E_x}{\partial y} \right] + \frac{\partial B_z}{\partial t} \right) dx \wedge dy \right] \wedge dt.$$

$$(10.2.1)$$

If we set $dF = 0$, each of the 3-form coefficients in (10.2.1) must equal zero. We can then retrieve Gauss's law for magnetism

$$\left(\frac{\partial B_x}{\partial x} + \frac{\partial B_y}{\partial y} + \frac{\partial B_z}{\partial z} \right) = 0$$

$$\Rightarrow \nabla \cdot \mathbf{B} = 0.$$

And Faraday's law

$$\left(\left[\frac{\partial E_z}{\partial y} - \frac{\partial E_y}{\partial z}\right] + \frac{\partial B_x}{\partial t}\right) dy \wedge dz$$

$$+ \left(\left[\frac{\partial E_x}{\partial z} - \frac{\partial E_z}{\partial x}\right] + \frac{\partial B_y}{\partial t}\right) dz \wedge dx$$

$$+ \left(\left[\frac{\partial E_y}{\partial x} - \frac{\partial E_x}{\partial y}\right] + \frac{\partial B_z}{\partial t}\right) dx \wedge dy = 0$$

$$\Rightarrow \nabla \times \mathbf{E} + \frac{\partial \mathbf{B}}{\partial t} = 0.$$

10.2.4 Gauss's law and the Ampère-Maxwell law

These two Maxwell equations are found by setting $d \star \mathsf{F} = \mathsf{J}$, where $\star\mathsf{F}$ is the Hodge dual of F :

$$\star\mathsf{F} = E_x dy \wedge dz + E_y dz \wedge dx + E_z dx \wedge dy + B_x dt \wedge dx + B_y dt \wedge dy + B_z dt \wedge dz,$$

and J is the current 3-form, which is derived from the current density $\mathbf{J}$ that we've already met. In four dimensions the components of the current density are

$$\mathbf{J} = (\rho, J_x, J_y, J_z).$$

We'll call the 1-form associated with this vector $\star\mathsf{J}$, where

$$\star\mathsf{J} = -\rho dt + J_x dx + J_y dy + J_z dz.$$

The first term on the right side is negative because the metric tensor for Minkowski space is non-Euclidean, with a minus sign in front of the time bit but not the space bits. The 1-form $\star\mathsf{J}$ is the Hodge dual of the thing we want, J, the current 3-form, where

$$\mathsf{J} = \rho dx \wedge dy \wedge dz - J_x dt \wedge dy \wedge dz - J_y dt \wedge dz \wedge dx - J_z dt \wedge dx \wedge dy. \quad (10.2.2)$$

Again, the minus signs crop up due to the implicit use of the Minkowski metric tensor.

So now we take the exterior derivative of $\star \mathsf{F}$:

$$d \star \mathsf{F} = \left(\frac{\partial E_x}{\partial x} dx + \frac{\partial E_x}{\partial y} dy + \frac{\partial E_x}{\partial z} dz + \frac{\partial E_x}{\partial t} dt \right) \wedge dy \wedge dz$$

$$+ \left(\frac{\partial E_y}{\partial x} dx + \frac{\partial E_y}{\partial y} dy + \frac{\partial E_y}{\partial z} dz + \frac{\partial E_y}{\partial t} dt \right) \wedge dz \wedge dx$$

$$+ \left(\frac{\partial E_z}{\partial x} dx + \frac{\partial E_z}{\partial y} dy + \frac{\partial E_z}{\partial z} dz + \frac{\partial E_z}{\partial t} dt \right) \wedge dx \wedge dy$$

$$+ \left(\frac{\partial B_x}{\partial x} dx + \frac{\partial B_x}{\partial y} dy + \frac{\partial B_x}{\partial z} dz + \frac{\partial B_x}{\partial t} dt \right) \wedge dt \wedge dx$$

$$+ \left(\frac{\partial B_y}{\partial x} dx + \frac{\partial B_y}{\partial y} dy + \frac{\partial B_y}{\partial z} dz + \frac{\partial B_y}{\partial t} dt \right) \wedge dt \wedge dy$$

$$+ \left(\frac{\partial B_z}{\partial x} dx + \frac{\partial B_z}{\partial y} dy + \frac{\partial B_z}{\partial z} dz + \frac{\partial B_z}{\partial t} dt \right) \wedge dt \wedge dz.$$

Again, many of these terms will drop out because $dx^i \wedge dx^i = 0$, and we get

$$\left(\frac{\partial E_x}{\partial x} + \frac{\partial E_y}{\partial y} + \frac{\partial E_z}{\partial z} \right) dx \wedge dy \wedge dz + \frac{\partial E_x}{\partial t} dt \wedge dy \wedge dz + \frac{\partial E_y}{\partial t} dt \wedge dz \wedge dx$$

$$+ \frac{\partial E_z}{\partial t} dt \wedge dx \wedge dy + \frac{\partial B_z}{\partial y} dy \wedge dt \wedge dz + \frac{\partial B_y}{\partial z} dz \wedge dt \wedge dy + \frac{\partial B_x}{\partial z} dz \wedge dt \wedge dx$$

$$+ \frac{\partial B_z}{\partial x} dx \wedge dt \wedge dz + \frac{\partial B_y}{\partial x} dx \wedge dt \wedge dy + \frac{\partial B_x}{\partial y} dy \wedge dt \wedge dx$$

$$= \left(\frac{\partial E_x}{\partial x} + \frac{\partial E_y}{\partial y} + \frac{\partial E_z}{\partial z} \right) dx \wedge dy \wedge dz + \left[\left(\frac{\partial E_x}{\partial t} - \left[\frac{\partial B_z}{\partial y} - \frac{\partial B_y}{\partial z} \right] \right) dt \wedge dy \wedge dz \right.$$

$$\left. + \left(\frac{\partial E_y}{\partial t} - \left[\frac{\partial B_x}{\partial z} - \frac{\partial B_z}{\partial x} \right] \right) dt \wedge dz \wedge dx + \left(\frac{\partial E_z}{\partial t} - \left[\frac{\partial B_y}{\partial x} - \frac{\partial B_x}{\partial y} \right] \right) dt \wedge dx \wedge dy \right]$$

$$= \nabla \cdot \mathbf{E} \, dx \wedge dy \wedge dz + \left[\left(\frac{\partial E_x}{\partial t} - [\nabla \times \mathbf{B}_x] \right) dt \wedge dy \wedge dz \right.$$

$$\left. + \left(\frac{\partial E_y}{\partial t} - [\nabla \times \mathbf{B}_y] \right) dt \wedge dz \wedge dx + \left(\frac{\partial E_z}{\partial t} - [\nabla \times \mathbf{B}_z] \right) dt \wedge dx \wedge dy \right].$$

Setting $d \star \mathsf{F}$ equal to J (10.2.2), and equating coefficients gives us the remaining two Maxwell equations.

First, Gauss's law:

$$\nabla \cdot \mathbf{E} \, dx \wedge dy \wedge dz = \rho dx \wedge dy \wedge dz$$

$$\Rightarrow \nabla \cdot \mathbf{E} = \rho.$$

And then the Ampère-Maxwell law:

$$\left(\frac{\partial E_x}{\partial t} - [\nabla \times \mathbf{B}_x]\right) dt \wedge dy \wedge dz$$

$$+ \left(\frac{\partial E_y}{\partial t} - [\nabla \times \mathbf{B}_y]\right) dt \wedge dz \wedge dx$$

$$+ \left(\frac{\partial E_z}{\partial t} - [\nabla \times \mathbf{B}_z]\right) dt \wedge dx \wedge dy$$

$$= -J_x dt \wedge dy \wedge dz - J_y dt \wedge dz \wedge dx - J_z dt \wedge dx \wedge dy$$

$$\Rightarrow \nabla \times \mathbf{B} - \frac{\partial \mathbf{E}}{\partial t} = \mathbf{J}.$$

11 Three nice results from topology

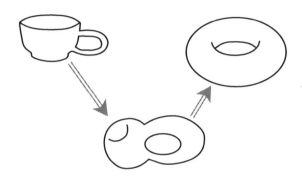

Figure 11.1: Not a hole lot of difference – coffee cup and doughnut.

Topology is that branch of mathematics concerned with the properties of shapes and spaces that are preserved through continuous distortions such as twisting and stretching. Hence the quip that a topologist is someone who cannot tell the difference between a coffee cup and a doughnut. Why? Because, conceptually at least, the drinking vessel can be smoothly deformed into the pastry – see Figure 11.1. A coffee cup or doughnut, however, cannot be transformed into a ball, because there is no hole in a ball and the allowable smooth deformations do not permit tearing, cutting or sewing edges together.

We can use the generalised Stokes' theorem to prove, by contradiction, three intriguing topological theorems, taken from Shifrin [20]. On the way, as an added bonus, we'll touch upon some slightly more abstract mathematics. These theorems are:

- the drum theorem
- the Brouwer fixed-point theorem
- the hairy ball theorem.

However, before tackling these proofs we need to lay a little groundwork.

First, following Shifrin's notation, we'll denote a point in $\mathbb{R}^n$ by $\mathbf{x}$, where $\mathbf{x}$ has coordinates $\left(x^1, x^2, x^3, \ldots, x^n\right)$.

Second, we'll use D^n to denote a closed unit ball in $\mathbb{R}^n$. The boundary of D^n is the unit sphere S^{n-1}, ie $\partial D^n = S^{n-1}$. So in $\mathbb{R}^2$, for example, if we draw a circle on a piece of paper, we have a two-dimensional unit ball (commonly called a disk) D^2, with a unit circle boundary S^1, ie $\partial D^2 = S^1$. In $\mathbb{R}^3$, we can think of a three-dimensional unit ball D^3, with a unit sphere boundary S^2, ie $\partial D^3 = S^2$. The closed unit ball D^3 consists of all points satisfying the inequality $x^2 + y^2 + z^2 \leq 1$. Harder for most of us to visualise, the closed unit ball D^n consists of all points satisfying the inequality $\left(x^1\right)^2 + \left(x^2\right)^2 + \left(x^3\right)^2 + \ldots + (x^n)^2 \leq 1$. Using the *unit* ball is for our convenience only. In fact, these theorems not only apply for a ball of any radius but also for any object that can be smoothly transformed into a ball.

Third, we need an n-form ω on S^n which has a non-zero integral. The following volume form fits the bill:

$$\omega = \sum_{i=1}^{n+1} (-1)^{i-1} x^i dx^1 \cdots \wedge dx^{(i-1)} \wedge dx^{(i+1)} \cdots \wedge dx^{n+1}. \qquad (11.0.1)$$

So for the unit circle S^1, $n = 1$ and we get

$$\omega = (-1)^0 \, x \, dy + (-1)^1 \, y \, dx$$
$$= -y \, dx + x \, dy. \qquad (11.0.2)$$

To see how this works, we can parameterise the unit circle using $\boldsymbol{\Phi}(t) = (\cos t, \sin t)$ for $0 \leq t \leq 2\pi$, giving tangent vectors

$$\frac{d\boldsymbol{\Phi}}{dt} = \left(\frac{dx}{dt}, \frac{dy}{dt}\right) = (-\sin t, \cos t).$$

We then integrate $\omega = -y \, dx + x \, dy$ over S^1 (the unit circle):

$$\int_{S^1} \omega = \int_{[0,2\pi]} \boldsymbol{\Phi}^* \omega = \int_0^{2\pi} \omega \left(\frac{d\boldsymbol{\Phi}}{dt}\right) dt$$

$$= \int_0^{2\pi} ((-\sin t \times -\sin t) + (\cos t \times \cos t)) \, dt$$

$$= \int_0^{2\pi} dt = 2\pi,$$

the circumference of the unit circle, which is definitely non-zero.

Similarly, we can use (11.0.1) to find ω for the unit sphere S^2. Here $n = 2$ and we get

$$\omega = (-1)^0 \, x \, dy \wedge dz + (-1)^1 \, y \, dx \wedge dz + (-1)^2 \, z \, dx \wedge dy$$
$$= x \, dy \wedge dz + y \, dz \wedge dx + z \, dx \wedge dy. \qquad (11.0.3)$$

We can parameterise the unit sphere using $\boldsymbol{\Phi}(u, v) = (\sin u \cos v, \sin u \sin v, \cos u)$ for $0 \leq u \leq \pi$ and $0 \leq v \leq 2\pi$. This eventually gives (for a region E of the uv plane)

$$\int_{S^2} \omega = \int_E \boldsymbol{\Phi}^* \omega = \int_0^{2\pi} \int_0^{\pi} \sin u \, du \, dv = 4\pi, \qquad (11.0.4)$$

the area of the unit sphere, which again is non-zero. You can check this result using the WolframAlpha online calculator [22] by typing the following into the input box and hitting Enter:

integrate (integrate (sin u) du from u = 0 to Pi) dv from v = 0 to 2*Pi

And so on, using (11.0.1) to find a non-zero integral n-form ω for any S^n.

The intuition behind (11.0.1) is as follows.

$\mathbb{R}^n$ has a standard volume form $dV = dx^1 \wedge dx^2 \cdots \wedge dx^n$. So, for example, $dV = dx \wedge dy \wedge dz$ is the volume form of $\mathbb{R}^3$ and returns the volume of the parallelepiped spanned by three vectors. Now, say we have a surface S in $\mathbb{R}^3$ with a unit normal vector field $\mathbf{v}$. If we feed $\mathbf{v}$ into dV, instead of having a 3-form measuring volume in $\mathbb{R}^3$, we have a 2-form measuring areas orthogonal to $\mathbf{v}$, ie the area of S.

Staying, in $\mathbb{R}^3$, let the surface S be the unit sphere S^2, which has a unit normal vector field $\mathbf{v} = (x, y, z) = x\hat{\mathbf{e}}_x + y\hat{\mathbf{e}}_y + z\hat{\mathbf{e}}_z$. We can write

$$dV = dx \wedge dy \wedge dz = dy \wedge dz \wedge dx = dz \wedge dx \wedge dy.$$

If we feed $\mathbf{v}$ into dV we get a 2-form ω, where

$$\omega = x\hat{\mathbf{e}}_x \left(dx \wedge dy \wedge dz \right) + y\hat{\mathbf{e}}_y \left(dy \wedge dz \wedge dx \right) + z\hat{\mathbf{e}}_z \left(dz \wedge dx \wedge dy \right)$$

$$= x\, dy \wedge dz + y\, dz \wedge dx + z\, dx \wedge dy,$$

ie (11.0.3), which as we saw above is a machine for measuring the area of the unit sphere.

Similarly, for the unit circle S^1 embedded in $\mathbb{R}^2$ and with a unit normal vector field $\mathbf{v} = (x, y) = x\hat{\mathbf{e}}_x + y\hat{\mathbf{e}}_y$. If we feed $\mathbf{v}$ into the volume form $dV = dx \wedge dy = -dy \wedge dx$ we get a 1-form ω, where

$$\omega = x\hat{\mathbf{e}}_x \left(dx \wedge dy \right) - y\hat{\mathbf{e}}_y \left(dy \wedge dx \right) = -y\, dx + x\, dy,$$

ie (11.0.2), which as we saw above is a machine for measuring the circumference of the unit circle.

We can extend this argument to S^n (embedded in $\mathbb{R}^{n+1}$, with volume form $dV = dx^1 \wedge dx^2 \cdots \wedge dx^{n+1}$) and which has a unit normal vector field $\mathbf{v} = \left(x^1, x^2, x^3, \ldots, x^{n+1} \right)$. When $\mathbf{v}$ acts on dV, each $x^i\mathbf{e}_i$ will remove a dx^i from dV and we end up with (11.0.1):

$$\omega = \sum_{i=1}^{n+1} (-1)^{i-1} x^i dx^1 \cdots \wedge dx^{(i-1)} \wedge dx^{(i+1)} \cdots \wedge dx^{n+1},$$

the integral of which tells us the 'area' of S^n orthogonal to $\mathbf{v}$, a non-zero quantity. The $(-1)^{i-1}$ coefficient, as we have seen, is there to give the right sign in front of the various terms after putting the differentials in the correct order . You will often see the notation

$$\omega = \iota_{\mathbf{v}} \left(dx^1 \wedge dx^2 \cdots \wedge dx^{n+1} \right) = \sum_{i=1}^{n+1} (-1)^{i-1} x^i dx^1 \cdots \wedge dx^{(i-1)} \wedge dx^{(i+1)} \cdots \wedge dx^{n+1},$$

where $\iota_{\mathbf{v}}$ denotes the interior product or contraction of a differential form with a vector field; in this case the differential form dV with the vector field $\mathbf{v}$.

Anticipating the proof of the drum theorem in the next section, we now need to ask what happens if we take the exterior derivative of ω. The somewhat surprising answer to that question is that the meaning of $d\omega$ depends on whether ω is on $\mathbb{R}^{n+1}$ or S^n. If ω is on $\mathbb{R}^{n+1}$, we can make use of the generalised Stokes' theorem (9.0.1) and write, for the unit ball D^{n+1} as a region of $\mathbb{R}^{n+1}$,

$$\int_{D^{n+1}} d\omega = \int_{S^n} \omega,$$

to give us the 'area' of S^n as discussed above. Taking D^3, for example, for $\omega = x\,dy \wedge dz + y\,dz \wedge dx + z\,dx \wedge dy$ (11.0.3), we would have

$$\int_{D^3} d\omega = \int_{S^2} \omega,$$

giving

$$\int_{D^3} d\left(x\,dy \wedge dz + y\,dz \wedge dx + z\,dx \wedge dy \right) = \int_{S^2} x\,dy \wedge dz + y\,dz \wedge dx + z\,dx \wedge dy = 4\pi,$$

in agreement with (11.0.4). However, if ω is on S^n itself (meaning ω only acts on vectors on, ie tangent to, S^n), then the integral of ω over S^n still gives the 'area' of S^n, but $d\omega = 0$. Why? Because ω is an n-form on S^n, $d\omega$ is an $(n+1)$-form on S^n, and the only $(n+1)$-form on S^n is 0.

11.1 The drum theorem

Figure 11.2: Stretched and torn drum skins.

This theorem states that there is no smooth function $g : D^{n+1} \to S^n$ with the property that $g(\mathbf{x}) = \mathbf{x}$ for all points $\mathbf{x}$ on S^n.

What does that mean? For simplicity's sake, let's first consider the case where we have a two-dimensional unit ball (or disk) D^2, with a unit circle boundary S^1. The notation $g : D^2 \to S^1$ signifies a function g that maps D^2 to S^1. In other words, g takes any point on the unit disk (including, of course, the boundary) as an input and gives a point on the boundary as an output. The required property $g(\mathbf{x}) = \mathbf{x}$ for all points $\mathbf{x}$ on S^n means that when we apply g to a point $\mathbf{x}$ on S^1, we get that same point as an output. Think of a drum consisting of a tightly stretched drum skin fixed to a circular rim. Our function g leaves every point on the boundary rim in place *and* sends every interior point on the drum skin to the boundary. Physically, we are attempting to pull the entire drum skin back to the rim. It doesn't take much imagination to see that this can't be done without tearing the drum skin (Figure 11.2). And what applies to D^2 and S^1 also applies to the general case of D^{n+1} and S^n. But how to prove this?

Discussion of a unit ball D^{n+1} with unit boundary S^n suggests that if we could find an n-form ϕ on D^{n+1} we could use the generalised Stokes' theorem (9.0.1)

$$\int_M d\phi = \int_{\partial M} \phi,$$

to write

$$\int_{D^{n+1}} d\phi = \int_{S^n} \phi. \tag{11.1.1}$$

Well, we have a function g from D^{n+1} to S^n. We also have an n-form ω (which has a non-zero integral) on S^n. We can therefore use g to pull back ω from S^n to D^{n+1} to give us ϕ, ie

$$\phi = g^*\omega.$$

(If necessary, refer back to Figure 7.1 to refresh your memory regarding pullbacks. Here $D^{n+1} \equiv M$, $S^n \equiv N$ and $g \equiv \mathbf{\Phi}$). We can then rewrite (11.1.1) as

$$\int_{D^{n+1}} d\left(g^*\omega\right) = \int_{S^n} g^*\omega. \tag{11.1.2}$$

We noted at the end of section 7.1.1 that the pullback of ω commutes with the exterior derivative, meaning we can rewrite (11.1.2) as

$$\int_{S^n} g^*\omega = \int_{D^{n+1}} d\left(g^*\omega\right) = \int_{D^{n+1}} g^*\left(d\omega\right) = 0, \tag{11.1.3}$$

because (as referenced at the end of the previous section) ω is an n-form on S^n itself (not on $\mathbb{R}^{n+1}$), meaning $d\omega = 0$. So far so good, but we haven't proved our theorem. The next step is to recognise that on the boundary S^n the function $g\left(\mathbf{x}\right) = \mathbf{x}$ is the identity function, a function whose output is the same as its input, ie

$$f\left(x\right) = x.$$

(Because we are attempting to leave every point of the circular drum rim in place while we stretch the drum skin back to its boundary.)

Crucially, the pullback of a differential form ω by the identity function is just ω. Again referring back to Figure 7.1, if $\mathbf{\Phi}$ is the identity function then clearly $\mathbf{\Phi}^*\omega = \omega$. So now we can rewrite (11.1.3) as

$$\int_{S^n} \omega = \int_{S^n} g^*\omega = \int_{D^{n+1}} d\left(g^*\omega\right) = \int_{D^{n+1}} g^*\left(d\omega\right) = 0.$$

And now we have a contradiction, as we have chosen the n-form ω to have a non-zero integral over S^n. Hence the theorem is proved.

Note that if we didn't require g to be the identity function on the boundary, ie $g\left(\mathbf{x}\right) = \mathbf{x}$ for all points $\mathbf{x}$ on S^n, (11.1.3) would be valid and there would be no proof by contradiction. It's perfectly possible have a smooth function $g : D^{n+1} \to S^n$, but you can't have such a function *plus* the requirement that every boundary point remains fixed.

11.2 The Brouwer fixed-point theorem

Figure 11.3: Brouwer fixed-point theorem – two-dimensions.

This theorem states that for a smooth function $f : D^n \to D^n$, there must be a point $\mathbf{x}$ on D^n that doesn't change, ie there must be a point where $f(\mathbf{x}) = \mathbf{x}$. In other words, every smooth function from D^n to itself has a fixed point.

A two-dimensional illustration of this theorem is shown in Figure 11.3. Make a smaller copy of an image and then place the copy anywhere within the original image's boundary. At least one point of the copy will lie exactly over the corresponding point of the original. In three dimensions, smoothly stir a milkshake with a spoon (careful not to cause any turbulence). No matter how long you stir for, at least one particle of the milkshake will end up in the same position where it started.

The theorem is intuitively obvious in one-dimension, where a closed unit ball D^n of radius one becomes a closed interval $[-1, 1]$ and the function $f : D^n \to D^n$ becomes $f : [-1, 1] \to [-1, 1]$. Unravelling the notation, all this means is that f is a function whose input and output varies from -1 to 1. The wavy line in Figure 11.4 shows one such function $f(x)$. From the diagram it's obvious that any $f(x)$ from the interval $[-1, 1]$ to the interval $[-1, 1]$ must cross the line $y = x$ at least once. All intersection points are fixed points where $f(x) = x$.

Now we want to prove this theorem is true in any dimension. To do that, assume the theorem is false, meaning for all points $\mathbf{x}$ on D^n, $\mathbf{x}$ is in a different position compared to $f(\mathbf{x})$. Next, define another function r, which takes a point on the closed unit ball D^n to the boundary S^{n-1} (we write $r : D^n \to S^{n-1}$). Referring to Figure 11.5, set $r(\mathbf{x})$ to be the point on the boundary at the end of the straight line starting at $f(\mathbf{x})$ and passing through $\mathbf{x}$. Obviously, when the point $\mathbf{x}$ is on the boundary S^{n-1}, it must

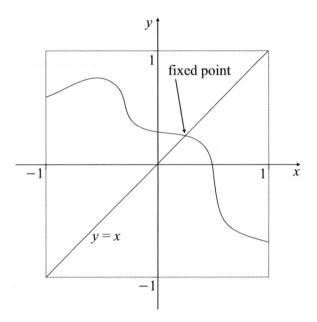

Figure 11.4: Brouwer fixed-point theorem – one-dimension.

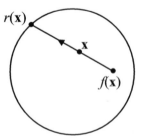

Figure 11.5: Brouwer fixed-point theorem – any dimension.

be that $r(\mathbf{x}) = \mathbf{x}$. However, by the previous drum theorem, we know that no such function exists. Therefore, f must have a fixed point.

11.3 The hairy ball theorem

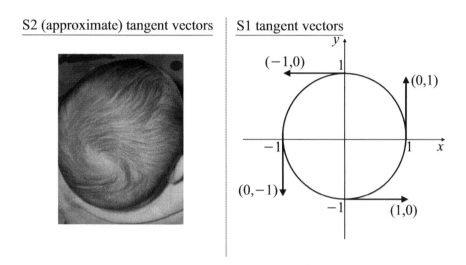

S2 (approximate) tangent vectors

S1 tangent vectors

Figure 11.6: Vanishing and nowhere-vanishing tangent vectors on S^2 and S^1.

This theorem states that there does not exist a nowhere-vanishing tangent vector field on the sphere S^n when n is even. Alternatively, if you have a hairy ball (a billiard ball, for example) you cannot comb the hairs continuously and end up with all the hairs lying flat along the surface. Figure 11.6 shows a vanishing 'tangent vector field' – aka hair – on the S^2 sphere of a baby's head. If we define m as a positive integer, we can denote an even-dimensional n-sphere by S^{2m}. The theorem then states that there does not exist a nowhere-vanishing tangent vector field on S^{2m}.

For a point $\mathbf{x}$ on S^n, a tangent vector field is a smooth function $\mathbf{v}(\mathbf{x})$ with the property that the dot product of $\mathbf{x}$ and $\mathbf{v}(\mathbf{x})$ is zero (because at any point on S^n the two vectors are perpendicular to each other), ie $\mathbf{x} \cdot \mathbf{v}(\mathbf{x}) = 0$. A nowhere-vanishing tangent vector field $\mathbf{v}(\mathbf{x})$ is possible on the unit circle S^1, as illustrated in Figure 11.6. For S^1, the tangent vector field is given by $\mathbf{v}(x) = (-y, x)$. So at the points $(1,0)$, $(0,1)$, $(-1,0)$ and $(0,-1)$ the tangent vectors are, respectively, $(0,1)$, $(-1,0)$, $(0,-1)$ and $(1,0)$. Clearly, for any point $\mathbf{x}$ on S^1,

$$\mathbf{x} \cdot \mathbf{v}(\mathbf{x}) = (x, y) \cdot (-y, x) = -xy + yx = 0.$$

Similarly, a nowhere-vanishing tangent vector field $\mathbf{v}(x)$ can be defined for any S^n where n is odd, because it is then possible to choose components of $\mathbf{v}(\mathbf{x})$ that cancel with $\mathbf{x}$ when taking the dot product $\mathbf{x} \cdot \mathbf{v}(\mathbf{x})$. For example, on S^3 (defined by $x^2 + y^2 + w^2 + z^2 = 1$) we could choose $\mathbf{v}(\mathbf{x}) = (-y, x, z, -w)$. The dot product with $\mathbf{x}$ then becomes

$$\mathbf{x} \cdot \mathbf{v}(\mathbf{x}) = (x, y, w, z) \cdot (-y, x, z, -w) = 0.$$

This method doesn't work for S^n when n is even. And, as we'll now show, it's *not* possible to construct a nowhere-vanishing tangent vector field on an even n S^n.

In order to prove the hairy ball theorem we need to introduce a concept that is fundamental to the study of smooth deformations – homotopy. Say we have two manifolds M and N, plus two smooth functions f and g from M to N. If f can be smoothly transformed into g, we say there is a homotopy between the two functions and that f and g are homotopic.

A smooth function $H(\mathbf{x}, t)$ for $0 \le t \le 1$ is a homotopy from f to g if, when $t = 0$ $H(\mathbf{x}, 0) = f(\mathbf{x})$, and when $t = 1$ $H(\mathbf{x}, 1) = g(\mathbf{x})$. Think of the parameter t as time. When we start the clock at $t = 0$, $H(\mathbf{x}, t)$ equals the function f. When we stop the clock when $t = 1$, $H(\mathbf{x}, t)$ has smoothly transformed into function g.

A couple of examples should make things clearer.

Example 11.1. Two functions f and g go from $\mathbb{R}$ (with single coordinate s) to $\mathbb{R}^2$ (with coordinates x and y). These functions are $f(s) = (s, s^2)$, ie $x = s$ and $y = s^2$, and $g(s) = (s, s)$, ie $x = s$ and $y = s$. Now consider the function $H(s, t) = (s, s^2 - ts^2 + ts)$. When $t = 0$, $H(s, 0) = (s, s^2)$, which is $f(s)$. When $t = 1$, $H(s, 1) = (s, s)$, which is $g(s)$. By increasing t from 0 to 1 we have smoothly transformed $f(s)$ to $g(s)$. The function $H(s, t) = (s, s^2 - ts^2 + ts)$ is a homotopy from f to g.

Example 11.2. The identity function $f : D^n \to D^n$, $f(\mathbf{x}) = \mathbf{x}$ means, by definition that if we feed a point $\mathbf{x}$ on D^n into f, out pops the same point $\mathbf{x}$. We have another function $g(\mathbf{x}) = 0$, meaning every time we feed a point $\mathbf{x}$ into g, out pops zero. The function $H(\mathbf{x}, t) = (1 - t)\mathbf{x}$ is a homotopy from f to g. When $t = 0$, $H(\mathbf{x}, 0) = \mathbf{x}$, which is f. When $t = 1$, $H(\mathbf{x}, 1) = 0$, which is g. By increasing t from 0 to 1 we have smoothly transformed f to g. Think of this homotopy as a movie that starts (when $t = 0$) with the unit ball D^n. As the film progresses, the ball shrinks to its centre until (at $t = 1$) it vanishes altogether.

Saying the same thing in slightly more abstract language, we can write a function

$$H : M \times [0, 1] \to N, \tag{11.3.1}$$

which is a rule that takes an element of the *product* of manifold M and the unit interval $[0, 1]$ and outputs an element of N. As explained above, we can understand H as

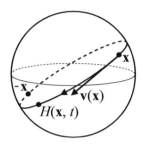

Figure 11.7: Homotopy $H(\mathbf{x}, t)$ on S^{2m}.

a smooth function $H(\mathbf{x}, t)$, which is a homotopy from f to g such that when $t = 0$ $H(\mathbf{x}, 0) = f(\mathbf{x})$, and when $t = 1$ $H(\mathbf{x}, 1) = g(\mathbf{x})$.

We have here introduced the idea of a product manifold. A cylinder, for example, is an open surface and is the product of a circle S^1 and an interval I. Think of either a collection of intervals arranged in a circle, or a collection of circles arranged along an interval. To denote this we write $S^1 \times I$, or $S^1 \times [0, 1]$ for the unit interval, which denotes a cylinder of height one. Another example of a product manifold is the torus, $S^1 \times S^1$, which is a closed surface formed by taking the product of two circles.

Using the generalised Stokes' theorem, it can be shown (a proof is given at the end of this section) that if M is a k-dimensional manifold without boundary, and ω is a closed (ie $d\omega = 0$) k-form on N, and if the smooth functions f and g from M to N are homotopic, then

$$\int\limits_M f^*\omega = \int\limits_M g^*\omega. \qquad (11.3.2)$$

We can now proceed to the proof of the hairy ball theorem.

We start by assuming the theorem is false and that there *does* exist a nowhere-vanishing unit tangent vector field $\mathbf{v}(\mathbf{x})$ on S^{2m}. We use $\mathbf{v}(\mathbf{x})$ to define a homotopy $H(\mathbf{x}, t)$ between the identity function $f : S^{2m} \to S^{2m}$, $f(\mathbf{x}) = \mathbf{x}$ and the antipodal function $g : S^{2m} \to S^{2m}$, $g(\mathbf{x}) = -\mathbf{x}$. The antipodal function means that if we feed a point $\mathbf{x}$ on S^n into g, out pops the point $-\mathbf{x}$ on the opposite (antipodal) side of the sphere. It turns out that a good candidate for $H(\mathbf{x}, t)$ is

$$H(\mathbf{x}, t) = (\cos \pi t)\, \mathbf{x} + (\sin \pi t)\, \mathbf{v}(\mathbf{x}). \qquad (11.3.3)$$

As shown in Figure 11.7, $H(\mathbf{x}, t)$ is the point πt radians from $\mathbf{x}$ along the great semicircle that runs in the direction of $\mathbf{v}(\mathbf{x})$ all the way to $-\mathbf{x}$.

As an example of how $H(\mathbf{x}, t)$ works, we can consider the constant upward pointing unit tangent vectors $\mathbf{v}(x, y, 0) = (0, 0, 1)$ on the equatorial circle of the unit sphere S^2. (11.3.3) then becomes

$$H((x, y, 0), t) = (\cos \pi t)(x, y, 0) + (\sin \pi t)(0, 0, 1).$$

The equatorial circle can be parameterised by $x = \cos s$, $y = \sin s$ for $0 \leq s \leq 2\pi$, giving

$$H(s, t) = (\cos \pi t)(\cos s, \sin s, 0) + (\sin \pi t)(0, 0, 1)$$

$$= ((\cos \pi t)(\cos s), (\cos \pi t)(\sin s), \sin \pi t).$$

So $x = (\cos \pi t)(\cos s)$, $y = (\cos \pi t)(\sin s)$ and $z = \sin \pi t$. Choosing a point $\mathbf{x}$ on the equatorial circle fixes s, meaning $\cos s$ and $\sin s$ are both constants. As t changes from 0 to 1, $H(x, y, t)$ moves on a line of longitude from $\mathbf{x} = (x, y, 0)$ on the equatorial circle, through the north pole to the point $-\mathbf{x} = (-x, -y, 0)$ on the opposite (antipodal) side of the sphere. If we set $s = 0$, for example, then

$$H(x, y, t) = (\cos \pi t, 0, \sin \pi t)$$

traces out an upper unit semicircle on the xz plane. And if we set $s = 1$, then

$$H(x, y, t) = (0, \cos \pi t, \sin \pi t)$$

traces out an upper unit semicircle on the yz plane.

The crux of all this is that if, on S^{2m}, we can show there is no homotopy $H(\mathbf{x}, t)$ between the identity function f and the antipodal function g, then there isn't a nowhere-vanishing unit tangent vector field $\mathbf{v}(\mathbf{x})$, and we have thus proved the theorem.

We make use of (11.3.2)

$$\int_{S^{2m}} f^* \omega = \int_{S^{2m}} g^* \omega.$$

And (11.0.1), which gives us the $2m$-form ω on S^{2m} whose integral is a non-zero integral

$$\omega = \sum_{i=1}^{2m+1} (-1)^{i-1} x^i dx^1 \cdots \wedge dx^{(i-1)} \wedge dx^{(i+1)} \cdots \wedge dx^{2m+1}. \tag{11.3.4}$$

We know that the pullback of a differential form ω by the identity function f is just ω, meaning

$$\int_{S^{2m}} \omega = \int_{S^{2m}} f^* \omega.$$

Knowing that $g(\mathbf{x}) = -\mathbf{x}$, we can calculate $g^* \omega$ using (11.3.4)

$$g^* \omega = g^* \left(\sum_{i=1}^{2m+1} (-1)^{i-1} x^i dx^1 \cdots \wedge dx^{(i-1)} \wedge dx^{(i+1)} \cdots \wedge dx^{2m+1} \right)$$

simply by putting a minus sign in front of all the relevant bits to give

$$g^*\omega = \sum_{i=1}^{2m+1} (-1)^{i-1} \left(-x^i\right) \left(-dx^1\right) \cdots \wedge \left(-dx^{(i-1)}\right) \wedge \left(-dx^{(i+1)}\right) \cdots \wedge \left(-dx^{2m+1}\right)$$

$$= (-1)^{2m+1} \omega$$

$$= -\omega.$$

And we can say

$$\int_{S^{2m}} \omega = \int_{S^{2m}} f^*\omega = \int_{S^{2m}} g^*\omega = - \int_{S^{2m}} \omega.$$

But this can only be true if

$$\int_{S^{2m}} \omega = 0,$$

which we know is false. Therefore, there is no homotopy $H(\mathbf{x}, t)$ between the identity function f and the antipodal function g, there *doesn't* exist a nowhere-vanishing unit tangent vector field $\mathbf{v}(\mathbf{x})$ on S^{2m}, and the theorem is proved.

On S^n, where n is odd, there does exist a nowhere-vanishing tangent vector field and there is a homotopy (11.3.3)

$$H(\mathbf{x}, t) = (\cos \pi t) \mathbf{x} + (\sin \pi t) \mathbf{v}(\mathbf{x})$$

between the identity function f and the antipodal function g.

11.3.1 Proof of Equation (11.3.2)

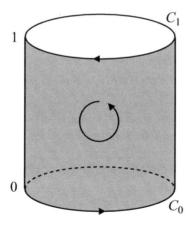

Figure 11.8: Cylinder $S^1 \times [0, 1]$.

If M is a k-dimensional manifold without boundary, and ω is a closed (ie $d\omega = 0$) k-form on N, and if the smooth functions f and g from M to N are homotopic, then (11.3.2) states

$$\int_M f^*\omega = \int_M g^*\omega.$$

We can prove this using the generalised Stokes' theorem.

Say we have two smooth functions f and g from S^1 to S^1, which we can write as $f, g : S^1 \to S^1$. If there is a homotopy H between f and g, we can, recalling (11.3.1), write this as

$$H : S^1 \times [0, 1] \to S^1,$$

where $S^1 \times [0, 1]$ is a cylinder of height one.

Figure 11.8 shows such a cylinder with a counterclockwise orientation as indicated by the little circular arrow. The boundary of the cylinder consists of the union of the two circular ends C_0 and C_1. But note that the induced orientation of the boundary circles C_0 and C_1 are in opposite directions. The bottom of the little circular arrow induces a counterclockwise orientation on C_0; the top of the little circular arrow induces a clockwise orientation on C_1.

A 1-form on S^1 with a non-zero integral is (11.0.2):

$$\omega = -y\,dx + x\,dy.$$

As we have a function H from $S^1 \times [0, 1]$ to S^1, we can pull back ω from S^1 to $S^1 \times [0, 1]$. We denote this pullback by $H^*\omega$. Now, using the generalised Stokes' theorem (9.0.1)

$$\int_M d\omega = \int_{\partial M} \omega,$$

we can write

$$\int_{\partial(S^1 \times [0,1])} H^*\omega = \int_{S^1 \times [0,1]} d\left(H^*\omega\right) = \int_{S^1 \times [0,1]} H^*\left(d\omega\right) = 0, \qquad (11.3.5)$$

because, as noted at the end of section 7.1.1, the pullback of ω commutes with the exterior derivative, and $d\omega$ is a 2-form on S^1 and therefore must equal zero.

The left-hand term in (11.3.5) denotes the integral of $H^*\omega$ over the cylinder's boundary $\partial\left(S^1 \times [0, 1]\right)$. As noted above, the boundary consists of the two circular ends, C_0 and C_1, which have the opposite induced orientations $-S^1 \times \{0\}$ and $S^1 \times \{1\}$. This can be written as

$$\partial\left(S^1 \times [0, 1]\right) = \pm\left(S^1 \times \{1\} - S^1 \times \{0\}\right).$$

The $\pm$ in front of the right-hand term reflects the fact that the decision to put a minus sign in front of $S^1 \times \{0\}$ and not $S^1 \times \{1\}$ is an arbitrary one. The key point is that the boundary circles $S^1 \times \{0\}$ and $S^1 \times \{1\}$ have opposite signs.

At the bottom of the cylinder, the integral of $H^*\omega$ over $\partial\left(S^1 \times [0,1]\right)$ is the same as the integral of $H^*\omega$ over $-S^1 \times \{0\}$, which is the same as the integral of $f^*\omega$ over $-S^1$. At the top of the cylinder, the integral of $H^*\omega$ over $\partial\left(S^1 \times [0,1]\right)$ is the same as the integral of $H^*\omega$ over $S^1 \times \{1\}$, which is the same as the integral of $g^*\omega$ over S^1. We can write this as

$$\int_{\partial(S^1\times[0,1])} H^*\omega = \int_{S^1\times\{1\}} H^*\omega - \int_{S^1\times\{0\}} H^*\omega = \int_{S^1} g^*\omega - \int_{S^1} f^*\omega = 0.$$

And thus

$$\int_{S^1} f^*\omega = \int_{S^1} g^*\omega.$$

The general result for a homotopy

$$H : M \times I \to N$$

between f and g is given by

$$\int_{\partial(M\times I)} H^*\omega = \int_{M\times\{1\}} H^*\omega - \int_{M\times\{0\}} H^*\omega = \int_{M} g^*\omega - \int_{M} f^*\omega = 0.$$

And thus

$$\int_{M} f^*\omega = \int_{M} g^*\omega,$$

which is what we set out to show.

And finally ...
If you liked this book, or even (perish the thought) if you didn't, then please consider helping other readers by posting a review on Amazon, Goodreads or other online book review site. All honest reviews are appreciated, whatever the length or rating. Thank you.

Bibliography

[1] Anon. (2014) URL `https://www.reddit.com/r/math/comments/26qya9/`

[2] Arapura, D. (2016) Introduction to Differential Forms. URL `https://www.math.purdue.edu/~dvb/preprints/diffforms.pdf`

[3] Arfken, G. B., Weber, H. J., Harris, F. E. (2013) Mathematical Methods for Physicists: A Comprehensive Guide.

[4] Arnold, V. I. (1989) Mathematical Methods of Classical Mechanics.

[5] Bachman, D. (2011) A Geometric Approach to Differential Forms.

[6] Baez, J. & Muniain, J. P. (1994) Gauge Fields, Knots and Gravity

[7] Bryan, K. (2016) Differential Forms. URL `https://www.rose-hulman.edu/~bryan/lottamath/difform.pdf`

[8] Edwards, C. H. (1995) Advanced Calculus of Several Variables.

[9] Fortney, J. P. (2018) A Visual Introduction to Differential Forms and Calculus on Manifolds.

[10] Frankel, T. (2004) The Geometry of Physics: An Introduction.

[11] Hubbard, J. H. & Burke Hubbard, B. (1998) Vector Calculus, Linear Algebra, and Differential Forms: A Unified Approach.

[12] Lee, J. M. (2002) Introduction to Smooth Manifolds.

[13] Math Insight. URL `https://mathinsight.org/`

[14] Misner, C. W., Thorne, K.S., Wheeler, J. A. (1973) Gravitation.

[15] Parkinson, C. (2014) The Elegance of Differential Forms in Vector Calculus and Electromagnetics. URL `https://chesterrep.openrepository.com/handle/10034/345818`

[16] Paul's Online Notes. URL `http://tutorial.math.lamar.edu/`

[17] Penrose, R. (2005) The Road to Reality.

[18] Schulz, A. E. & Schulz, W. C. (2016) A Practical Introduction to Differential Forms. URL `https://www.cefns.nau.edu/~schulz/tril.pdf`

[19] Schutz, B. (2009) A First Course in General Relativity.

[20] Shifrin, T. (2005) Multivariable Mathematics: Linear Algebra, Multivariable Calculus, and Manifolds.

[21] Spivak, M. (1999) A Comprehensive Introduction to Differential Geometry, Vol 1.

[22] WolframAlpha Calculus and Analysis Calculator. URL `http://www.wolframalpha.com/examples/Calculus.html`

Index

identity function, 132, 136
infinitesimals and tangent vectors, 28
integration, 75
    coordinate-independence, 75
    defining, 82
    examples, 86
integration, and vector calculus, 95
integration, the recipe, 86
interior product, 130

Jacobian matrix, 41, 77

Kronecker delta, 29

Lee, 38
Lee, J. M., 107
line integrals, *see* vector calculus

magnetic field, 117
magnetic field 2-form, 122
manifold, product, 137
manifolds, 15, 18, 29
    boundary, 16, 73, 107
    integration on, 75, 107
    orientation, 69
Maxwell's equations, 117
metric tensor, 57, 120, 124
multilinear function, 23, 42, 48, 53

orientation, 43, 69
    induced, 73, 82
    positive/negative, 69
    vector space, 69

parallelepiped, 23
parallelogram, 22
parallelotope, 24
parameterisation, 19
parameterisation, independence of, 92
Parkinson, C., 73
Penrose, R., 117
polar coordinates, 31
proof by contradiction, 127
pullback, 79, 82, 132

scalar fields, 35

Schulz, A. E. & Schulz, W. C., 13, 79, 89, 107
Shifrin, T., 127
signed area, 23, 46
signed volume, 23
spherical coordinates, 91
Spivak, M., 28, 36
Stokes' theorem, 112
Stokes' theorem, generalised, 107, 127
surface integrals, *see* vector calculus

tangent space, 18, 29
tangent vectors, 18, 50, 54
    to a circle, 33
    to a curve, 34
topology, 127

vector calculus
    line integrals, 96
    surface integrals, 100
    volume integrals, 105
vector fields, 18
    corresponding differential forms, 57
vector identities, 68
vector space, 18, 30
    orientation, 69
vectors, 17
    acting on forms, notation, 20
    unit normal, 72, 101
volume form, 84, 89, 128
volume integrals, *see* vector calculus

wedge product, 42, 43
work form, 42

Printed in Great Britain
by Amazon

17772471R00084